To: Flag Officer in Charge of Lindisfarne Base
From: Drongo Kane
Subject: Piratical action by Lieutenant Commander
John Grimes

Sir,

I regret to have to report that while my vessel was proceeding on her lawful occasions she was wantonly attacked by your Seeker, under the command of your Lieutenant Grimes. Commander Grimes not only used his armament to impede the embarkation of fare-paying passengers, subjecting them to a sleep gas barrage, but also fired upon *Southerly Buster* herself. Later he attempted to ram my ship after she had lifted off . . .

GRIMES IS AT IT AGAIN!

THE INHERITORS

A. BERTRAM CHANDLER

ace books
A Division of Charter Communications Inc.
A GROSSET & DUNLAP COMPANY
360 Park Avenue South
New York, New York 10010

An ACE Book

Cover art by Paul Alexandra

This Ace printing: June 1978

Printed in U.S.A.

For my favorite aelurophobe

Grimes was on the carpet—neither for the first nor the last time.

He stood stiffly in front of the vast, highly polished desk behind which sat Admiral Buring, of the Federation's Survey Service. His prominent ears were angrily flushed but his rugged face was expressionless.

The admiral's pudgy hands played with the bulky folder that was before him. His face, smooth and heavy, was as expressionless as Grimes's. His voice was flat.

He said, "Commodore Damien warned me about you when you were transferred to my command. Not that any warning was necessary. For one so young you have achieved a considerable degree of notoriety." He paused expectantly, but Grimes said nothing. Buring continued, but now with a hint of feeling in his voice. "My masters—who, incidentally, are also yours—are far from amused at your latest antics. You know—you *should* know—that interference, especially by junior officers, in the internal affairs of any world whatsoever, regardless of the cultural or technological level of the planet in question, is not tolerated. I concede that there were extenuating circumstances, and that the new rulers of Sparta speak quite highly of you. . . .'' The thick eyebrows, like furry, black caterpillars, arched incredulously. "Nonetheless . . .''

The silence was so thick as to be almost tangible. Grimes decided that it was incumbent upon himself to break it.

"Sir?"

"Nonetheless, Lieutenant Commander, your continued presence at Base is something of an embarrassment, especially since a party of vips, political vips at that, is due here very shortly. Some commission or other, touring the galaxy at the taxpayer's expense. I don't want you around so that politicians can ask you silly questions—to which, I have no doubt, you would give even sillier answers.

"Furthermore, this whole Spartan affair has blown up into a minor crisis in interplanetary politics. Both the Duchy of Waldegren and the Empire of Waverley are talking loudly about spheres of influence." The admiral allowed himself the suspicion of a smile. "In any sort of crisis, Grimes, there is one thing better than presence of mind. . . ."

"And that is, sir?" asked Grimes at last.

"Absence of body. Ha. So I'm doing you a good turn, sending you out in *Seeker*, on a Lost Colony hunt. There have been persistent rumors of one out in the Argo Sector. Go and find it—or get lost yourself. I'm easy."

"Maintenance, sir . . ." said Grimes slowly. "Repairs . . . stores . . . manning. . . ."

"They're your business, Captain. No, I'm not promoting you, merely according you the courtesy title due to the commanding officer of a ship. You look after those no doubt boring details. And"—he made a major operation of looking at his watch—"I want you off Lindisfarne by sixteen-hundred hours local time tomorrow."

Grimes looked at his own watch. He had just seventeen hours, twelve minutes and forty-three seconds in which to ensure that his ship was, in all respects, ready for space. Maintenance, he knew, was well in hand. There were no crew deficiencies. Taking aboard essential stores would not occupy much time.

Even so . . .

"I'd better be getting on with it, sir," he said.

"You'd bloody well better. I'll send your orders down to you later."

Grimes put on his cap, saluted smartly and strode out of the admiral's office.

2

She was a survey ship rather than a warship, was *Seeker*. The Survey Service, in its first beginnings, had been just that—a survey service. But aliens being what they are—and humans being what *they* are—police work, on large and small scales, had tended to become more important than mere exploration and charting. The Survey Service, however, had not quite forgotten its original function. It maintained a few ships designed for peaceful rather than warlike pursuits, and *Seeker* was a member of this small squadron. Nonetheless, even she packed quite a wallop.

Lieutenant Commander John Grimes was her captain. His last assignment, during which he had stumbled upon a most peculiar Lost Colony, had been census taking. Now he had been actually sent out to *find* a Lost Colony. He suspected that *anything* might happen, and probably would. It wasn't that he was accident prone. He was just a catalyst.

Nothing had happened yet; after all, it was early in the voyage. He had lifted from Lindisfarne exactly on time, driving through the atmosphere smoothly and easily, maintaining his departure trajectory until he was clear of the Base Planet's Van Allens. Then, with the inertial drive shut down, the ship had been turned about her short axis until she was lined up, with due allowance for drift, on the target star. The Mannschenn Drive had been started, the inertial drive restarted—and passage was commenced.

Satisfied, he had filled and lit his pipe, and when it was going well had ordered, "Deep space routine, Mr. Saul." He had made his way to his quarters below and abaft the control room and then, ensconced in his easy chair, had opened the envelope containing his orders.

The first sheet of the bundle of papers had contained nothing startling. *You will proceed to the vicinity of the star Gamma Argo and conduct a preliminary survey of the planets in orbit about same, devoting especial attention to any of such bodies capable of supporting human life.* "Mphm . . ." he grunted. The rest of the page consisted of what he referred to as "the usual guff."

At the head of the next page was the sentence that brought an expression of interest to his face. *We have reason to believe that there is a humanoid—or possibly human—settlement on the fourth planet of this system. Should this settlement exist it is probable that it is a hitherto undiscovered Lost Colony. You are reminded that your duties are merely to conduct an investigation, and that you are not, repeat not, to interfere in the internal affairs of the colony.*

"Mphm," grunted Grimes again. Noninterference was all very well, but at times it was hard to

5

maintain one's status as a mildly interested spectator.

Appended hereto are reports from our agents at Port Llangowan, on Siluria, at Port Brrooun, on Drroomoorr, at Port Mackay, on Rob Roy, at Port Forinbras, on Elsinore, at . . .

"Mphm." The Intelligence Branch seemed to be earning its keep, for a change. Grimes turned to the first report and read:

From Agent X1783 (Commander, I.B., F.S.S.)
Dated at Port Llangowan, May 5, Year 171 Silurian (17/13/57 TS)
To O.I.C. Intelligence, Federation's Survey Service, Port Woomera, Centralia, Earth.
Sir,

POSSIBLE LOST COLONY IN ARGO SECTOR

I have to report the possibility that there is a hitherto undiscovered Lost Colony in the Argo Sector, apparently on a planet in orbit about Gamma Argo.

It is my custom, whilst stationed on this world, to spend my evenings in the Red Dragon tavern, a hostelry that seems to be the favorite drinking place of whatever merchant spacemen are in port.

On the evening of May 3 several officers from the Dog Star Line's Pomeranian were lined up at the bar, and were joined there by officers of the same company's Corgi, newly berthed. As was to be expected, the personnel of the two vessels were old friends or acquaintances.

The table at which I was seated was too far from

the bar for me to overhear the conversation, but I was able to make use of my Mark XVII recorder, playing the recording back later that night in the privacy of my lodgings. The spool has been sent to you under separate cover, but herewith is a suitably edited transcript of what was said, with everything of no importance—e.g. the usual friendly blasphemies, obscenities and petty company gossip—deleted.

First Mate of Pomeranian: *And where the hell have you been hiding yourselves? You should have been in before us. I suppose that you got lost.*

Second Mate of Corgi: *I never get lost.*

First Mate of Pomeranian: *Like hell you don't. I remember when you got your sums wrong when we were together in the old* Dalmation, *and we finished up off Hamlet instead of Macbeth. . . . But what's twenty light-years between friends?*

Second Mate of Corgi: *I told you all that the computer was on the blink, but nobody would listen to me. As for this trip, we had to deviate.*

First Mate of Corgi: *Watch it, Peter!*

Second Mate of Corgi: *Why?*

First Mate of Corgi: *You know what the old man told us.*

Second Mate of Corgi: *Too bloody right I do. He's making his own report to the general manager, with copies every which way. Top Secret. For your eyes only. Destroy by fire before reading. He's wasted in the Dog Star Line. He should have been in the so-called Intelligence Branch of the clottish Survey Service.*

First Mate of Pomeranian: *What did happen?*

First Mate of Corgi: *Nothing much. Mannschenn Drive slightly on the blink, so we had to find a suitable planet on which to park our arse while we recalibrated.*

Second Mate of Corgi: *And what a planet! You know how I like* sleek *women. . . .*

First Mate of Corgi: *Watch it, you stupid bastard!*

Second Mate of Corgi: *Who're you calling a bastard? You can sling your rank around aboard the bloody ship, but not here. If I'd had any sense I'd'a skinned out before the bitch lifted off. Morrowria'll do me when I retire from the Dog Star Line! Or resign . . .*

First Mate of Corgi: *Or get fired—as you will be, unless you pipe down!*

Second Mate of Corgi: *You can't tell me . . .*

First Mate of Corgi: *I can, and I bloody well am telling you! Come on, finish your drink, and then back to the ship!*

At this juncture there are sounds of a scuffle as Corgi's *chief officer, a very big man, hustles his junior out of the Red Dragon.*

Third Mate of Pomeranian: *What the hell was all that about?*

First Mate of Pomeranian: *Search me.*

The rest of the recorded conversation consists of idle and futile speculation by Pomeranian's *officers as to the identity of the world landed upon by* Corgi.

To date I have been unable to identify this planet myself. There is no Morrowvia listed in the catalogue, even when due allowance is made for variations in spelling. Also I have checked the Navy

List, and found that the master of Corgi is not, and never has been, an officer in the FSS Reserve. None of his officers hold a Reserve commission. It may be assumed, therefore, that the master's report on the discovery of what appears to be a Lost Colony will be made only to his owners.

Corgi, *when she deviated, was bound from Darnstadt to Siluria. Her normal trajectory would have taken her within three light-years of Gamma Argo. The planetary system of Gamma Argo was surveyed in the early days of the Second Expansion, and no indigenous intelligent life was found on any of its worlds. . . .*

"Mphm . . ." Grimes refilled and relit his pipe. This was interesting reading.

He turned to the report from the agent at Port Brrooun. He, the shipping advisor to the Terran Consul, had been spending most of his free evenings in an establishment called the Beer Hive. Brrooun had been *Corgi's* next port of call after Llangowan. Her second officer had confined his troubles to a sympathetic Shaara drone. At Port Mackay, on Rob Roy, he had gotten fighting drunk on the local whiskey and had beaten up the chief officer and publicly abused the master. Normally such conduct would have led to his instant dismissal—but Captain Danzellan, of *Corgi*, had been most reluctant to leave the objectionable young man behind, in the hands of the civil authorities. The Intelligence Officer at Port Mackay, although knowing nothing of the Lost Colony, had been intrigued by the failure of the master to rid himself of an obvious malcontent and had wondered what was behind it. His own theories, for what they were worth, included a Hanoverian plot against the Jacobean royal house of Waverley. . . .

It was from Port Fortinbras, on Elsinore, that the next really interesting report came. The agent there was a woman, and worked as a waitress in the Poor Yorick, a tavern famous for its funereal decor. The agent, too, was famous insofar as the Intelligence Branch of the Survey Service was concerned, being known as the Bug Queen. Her specialty was recorders printed into the labels on bottles.

Transcript of conversation between Harald Larsen, owner-manager of Larsen's Repair Yard, and Peter Dalquist, owner of Dalquist's Ship Chandlery:

Dalquist: An' how are things at the yard, Harald?

Larsen: Can't complain, Pete, can't complain. Southerly Buster's *havin' a face lift.*

Dalquist: Drongo Kane . . .

Larsen: You can say what you like about Drongo— but he always pays his bills. . . .

Dalquist: Yeah. But he drives a hard bargain first.

Larsen: You can say that again.

Dalquist: An' what is it this time? General maintenance? Survey?

Larsen: Modifications. He's havin' his cargo spaces converted into passenger accommodation—of a sort. An' you remember those two quick-firin' cannon I got off that derelict Waldegren gunboat? Drongo's havin' 'em mounted on the Buster.

Dalquist: But it ain't legal. Southerly Buster's *a merchant ship.*

Larsen: Drongo says that it is legal, an' that he's entitled to carry defensive armament. . . . Some o' the places he gets to, he needs it! But I checked up with me own legal eagles just to make sure that me own jets are clear. They assured me that Drongo's within his rights.

Dalquist: But quick-firin' cannon, when every man-o'-war is armed to the teeth with laser, misguided missiles an' only the Odd Gods of the Galaxy know what else! Doesn't make sense.

Larsen: Maybe it doesn't–but Drongo's got too much sense to take on a warship.

Dalquist: What if a warship takes on him?

Larsen: That's his worry.

Dalquist: But he must be thinkin' of fightin' somebody. . . . Any idea who it might be?

Larsen: I haven't a clue. All that I know is that his last port, before he came here, was Brrooun, on one o' the Shaara worlds. He told me–he'd had rather too much to drink himself–that he'd fed a couple of bottles of Scotch to a talkative drone. He said that he'll buy drinks for anybody–or anything–as long as he gets information in return. Anyhow, this drone told Drongo what he'd been told by the drunken second mate of a Dog Star tramp. . . .

Dalquist: Which was?

Larsen: Drongo certainly wasn't telling me, even though he'd had a skinful. He did mutter something about Lost Colonies, an' finders bein' keepers, an' about the Dog Star Line havin' to be manned by greyhounds if they wanted to get their dirty paws into this manger. . . .

Dalquist: An' was that all?
Larsen: You said it. He clammed up.

Unfortunately Captain Kane and his officers, un-like the majority of spacemen visiting Port Fortin-bras, do not frequent the Poor Yorick, preferring the King Claudius. On the several occasions that I have been there as a customer, at the same times as Southerly Buster's *personnel, I have been unable to learn anything of importance. Attempts made by myself to strike up an acquaintance with Captain Kane, his mates and his engineers have failed.*

Grimes chcukled. He wondered what the Bug Queen looked like. It seemed obvious that she owed her success as an agent to her skill with electronic gadgetry rather than to her glamour. But Kane? Where did *he* come into the picture? The man was notorious—but, to date, had always managed to stay on the right side of the law.

But it was time that he, Grimes, put his senior officers into the picture.

3

They were all in Grimes's day cabin—his departmental heads and his senior scientific officers. There was Saul, the first lieutenant, a huge, gentle, very black man. There was Connery, chief engineer. The two officers in charge of communications were there—Timmins, the electronicist, and Hayakawa, the psionicist. There were Doctors Tallis, Westover and Lazenby—biologist, geologist and ethologist respectively—all of whom held the rank of full commander. Forsby—physicist—had yet to gain his doctorate and was only a lieutenant. There were Lieutenant Pitcher, navigator, Lieutenant Stein, ship's surgeon and bio-chemist, and Captain Philby, officer in charge of *Seeker's* Marines.

Grimes, trying to look and to feel fatherly, surveyed his people. He was pleased to note that the *real* spacemen—with the exception of Hayakawa—looked the part. Ethnic origins and differentiation of skin pigmentation were canceled out, as it were, by the common uniform. With the exception of Maggie Lazenby the scientists looked their part. They were, of course, all in uniform—though it wasn't what they were wearing but how they were wearing it that mattered. To them uniform was just something to cover their nakedness, the more comfortably the better. And to them beards were merely the means whereby the bother of depilation could be avoided. The growths sprouting from the faces of Tallis, Westover and Forsby contrasted shockingly with the neat hirsute adornments sported by Connery and Stein. The only one of the scientists at whom it was a pleasure to look was Doctor Lazenby—slim, auburn-haired and wearing a skirt considerably less than regulation length.

Grimes looked at her.

She snapped, "Get on with it, John." (Everybody present knew that she was a privileged person.)

"Mphm," he grunted as he carefully filled his pipe. "Help yourselves to coffee—or to something stronger from the bar, if you'd rather." He waited until everybody was holding a glass or a cup, then said, "As you all know by this time, this is a Lost Colony expedition. . . ."

Forsby raised his hand for attention. "Captain, forgive my ignorance, but I've only just joined the Survey Service. And I'm a physicist, not a historian. Just what *is* a Lost Colony?"

"Mphm," grunted Grimes again. He shot a dirty look at Maggie Lazenby as he heard her whispered *"Keep it short!"* He carefully lit his pipe. He said, "The majority of the so-called Lost Colonies date from the days of the Second Expansion, of the gaussjammers. The gaussjammers were interstellar ships that used the Ehrenhaft Drive. Cutting a long and involved story short, the Ehrenhaft generators produced a magnetic current—a current, not a field—and the ship in which they were mounted became, in effect, a huge magnetic particle, proceeding at a speed which could be regulated from a mere crawl to FTL along the "tramlines,' the lines of magnetic force. This was all very well—but a severe magnetic storm could throw a jaussjammer light-years off course, very often into an unexplored and uncharted sector of the galaxy. . . ."

"FTL?" demanded Forsby in a pained voice. "FTL?"

"A matter of semantics," Grimes told him airily. "You know, and I know, that faster-than-light speeds are impossible. With our Mannschenn Drive, for example, we cheat—by going astern in time as we're going ahead in space. The gaussjammers cheated too—by coexisting with themselves all along the lines of magnetic force that they were on. The main thing was—it worked. Anyhow, visualize a gaussjammer after a magnetic storm has tangled the lines of force like so much spaghetti *and* drained the micro-pile of all energy. The captain doesn't know where he is. But he has got power for his main engines."

"You said that the micro-pile was dead."

"Sure. But those ships ran to emergency generators—diesel generators. They churned out the electricity to drive the Ehrenhaft generators. The ship's biochemist knew the techniques for producing diesel fuel from whatever was available—even though it meant that all hands would be on short rations. So, for as long as she could, the ship either tried to make her way back to some known sector or to find a planet capable of being settled. . . ."

"Analogous," contributed Maggie Lazenby, "to the colonization of many Pacific islands by Polynesians in Earth's remote past. But this colony that we're supposed to be looking for, John . . ."

"Yes. I was getting around to that. It's supposed to be in the Argo Sector. It was stumbled upon by a Dog Star Line ship that made a deviation to recalibrate her Mannschenn Drive controls. It won't be a Lost Colony for much longer."

"Why not?" asked Forsby.

"To begin with, the Dog Star Line people know about it. The Shaara know about it. *We* know about it. And Drongo Kane knows about it."

"Drongo Kane?" This was Forsby again, of course. "Who's he?"

Grimes sighed. He supposed that his physicist knew his own subject, but he seemed to know very little outside it. He turned his regard to his officers, said, "Tell him."

"Drongo Kane . . ." murmured Saul in his deep, rich voice. "Smuggler, gunrunner . . ."

"Pirate . . ." contributed Timmins.

"That was never proven," Grimes told him.

"Perhaps not, sir. But I was on watch—it was when I was a junior in *Scorpio*—when *Bremerhaven*'s distress call came through."

"Mphm. As I recall it, *Bremerhaven*'s own activities at the time were somewhat dubious. . . ."

"Slaver . . ." said Saul.

16

"Somebody had to take the people off Ganda before the radiation from their sun fried them. Whatever ships were available had to be employed."

"But Kane was *paid* by the Duke of Waldegren for the people he carried in *Southerly Buster*."

"Just a fee," said Grimes, "or commission, or whatever, for the delivery of indentured labor."

"What about this bloody Lost Colony?" demanded Maggie Lazenby.

"We're supposed to find it." Grimes gestured toward the folder on his desk with the stem of his pipe. "I've had copies made of all the bumf that was given to me. It consists mainly of reports made by agents on quite a few worlds. Our man at Port Llangowan, on Siluria, recorded a conversation between officers of *Corgi* and *Pomeranian* in one of the local pubs. *Corgi* had found this world—which seems to be called Morrowvia—quite by chance. Our man at Port Brrooun, on Drroomoorr, recorded a conversation between the second mate of *Corgi* and a Shaara drone; once again Morrowvia was mentioned. The same young gentleman—the second mate, not the drone—got into trouble at Port Mackay on Rob Roy. Normally he'd have been emptied out there and then by *Corgi*'s master—but keeping him on board must have been the lesser of two evils."

"Why?" asked Forsby.

"Because," Grimes told him patiently, "the master of *Corgi* didn't want word of a new world that could well be included in the Dog Star Line's economic empire spread all over the galaxy. Where was I? Yes. Our woman at Port Fortinbras, on Elsinore, recorded a conversation between the owner of a repair yard and the owner of a ship chandlery. The repair yard was doing some work on Drongo Kane's ship, *Southerly Buster*—the mounting of armament, among other things. Kane had told the owner of the yard something—not much, but something—about a Lost Colony found by a Dog Star tramp. . . .''

"And what are *we* supposed to do, Captain?" asked Forsby. "Plant the Federation's flag, or something?"

"Or something," said Maggie Lazenby. "You can rest assured of that."

Or something, thought Grimes.

4

As far as Grimes knew there was no real urgency—nonetheless he pushed *Seeker* along at her maximum safe velocity. This entailed acceleration slightly in excess of 1.5 G, with a temporal precession rate that did not quite, as Maggie Lazenby tartly put it, have all hands and the cook living backward. But Maggie had been born and reared on Arcadia, a relatively low gravity planet and, furthermore, disliked and distrusted the time-twisting Mannschenn Drive even more than the average spaceman or—woman. However, Lieutenant Brian Connery was an extremely competent engineer and well able to maintain the delicate balance between the ship's main drive units without remotely endangering either the vessel or her personnel.

Even so, Grimes suffered. *Seeker* had a mixed crew—and a ship, as Grimes was fond of saying, is not a Sunday School outing. On past voyages it had been tacitly assumed that Maggie was the captain's lady. On this voyage it was so assumed too—by everybody except one of the two people most intimately concerned. Grimes tried to play along with the assumption, but it was hopeless.

"I suppose," he said bitterly, after she had

strongly resisted a quite determined pass, "that you're still hankering after that beefy lout, Brasidus or whatever his name was, on Sparta. . . ."

"No," she told him, not quite truthfully. "No. It's just that I can't possibly join in your fun and games when I feel as though I weigh about fourteen times normal."

"Only one and a half times," he corrected her.

"It *feels* fourteen times. And it's the psychological effect that inhibits me."

Grimes slumped back in his chair, extending an arm to his open liquor cabinet.

"Lay off it!" she told him sharply.

"So I can't drink now."

"You will not drink now." Her manner softened. "Don't forget, John, that you're responsible for the ship and everybody aboard her. . . ."

"Nothing can happen in deep space."

"Can't it?" Her fine eyebrows lifted slightly. "Can't it? After some of the stories I've heard, and after some of the stories you've told me yourself . . ."

"Mphm." He reached out again, but it was a half-hearted attempt.

"Things will work out, John," she said earnestly. "They always do, one way or the other. . . ."

"Suppose it's the wrong way?"

"You'll survive. I'll survive. We'll survive." She quoted, half seriously, " 'Men have died, and worms have eaten 'em—but not for love. . . .' "

"Where's that from?" he asked, interested.

"Shakespeare. You trade school boys—you're

20

quite impossible. You know nothing—*nothing*—outside your own field.''

''I resent that,'' said Grimes. ''At the Academy we had to do a course in Twentieth Century fiction. . . .''

Again the eyebrows lifted. ''You surprise me.'' And then she demanded incredulously, ''What sort of fiction?''

''It was rather specialized. Science fiction, as a matter of fact. Some of those old buggers made very good guesses. Most of them, though, were way off the beam. Even so, it was fascinating.''

''And still trade-school-oriented.''

He shrugged. ''Have it your way, Maggie. We're just Yahoos. But we do get our ships around.'' He paused, then delivered his own quotation. '' 'Transportation is civilization.' ''

''All right,'' she said at last. ''Who wrote that?''

''Kipling.''

''Kipling—and science fiction?''

''You should catch up on your own reading some time. . . .'' The telephone buzzed sharply. He got up and went rapidly to the handset.

She remarked sweetly, *''Nothing* can happen in deep space. . . .''

''Captain here,'' said Grimes sharply.

Lieutenant Hayakawa's reedy voice drifted into the day cabin. ''Hayakawa, Captain sir. . . .''

''Yes, Mr. Hayakawa?''

''I . . . am not certain. But I think I have detected psionic radiation—not close, but not too far distant. . . .''

"It is extremely unlikely," Grimes said, "that we are the only ship in this sector of space."

"I . . . I know, Captain. But—it is all vague, and the other telepath is maintaining a block. . . . I . . . I tried at first to push through, and he knew that I was trying. . . . Then, suddenly, I relaxed. . . ."

Psionic judo . . . thought Grimes.

"Yes. . . . You could call it that. . . . But there is somebody aboard that ship who is thinking all the time about . . . Morrowvia. . . ."

"Drongo Kane," said Grimes.

"No, Captain. Not Drongo Kane. This is a . . . young mind. Immature. . . ."

"Mphm. Anything else?"

"Yes. . . . He is thinking, too, of somebody called Tabitha. . . ."

"And who's *she* when she's up and dressed?"

"She is not dressed . . . not as *he* remembers her."

"This," stated Maggie Lazenby, "is disgusting. I thought, in my innocence, that the Rhine Institute took a very dim view of any prying by its graduates into private thoughts. I was under the impression that telepathy was to be used *only* for instantaneous communications over astronomical distances."

"If every Rhine Institute graduate who broke the Institute's rules dropped dead right now," Grimes told her, "there'd be one helluva shortage of trained telepaths. In any case, the Institute allows some latitude to those of its people who're in the employ of a recognized law enforcement agency. The Federation's Survey Service is one such. Conversely, the

Institute recognizes the right of any telepath, no matter by whom employed, to put up a telepathic block.''

"I still don't like it. Any of it.''

"Mr. Hayakawa,'' said Grimes into the telephone, ''you heard all that?''

"Yes, Captain.''

"And what are *your* views?''

In reply came a thin chuckle, then, ''I try to be loyal, sir. To the Institute, to the Service, to my shipmates, to my captain. Sometimes it is hard to be loyal to everybody at once. But, also, I try to be loyal to myself.''

"Putting it briefly,'' said Maggie Lazenby, ''you know on which side your bread is buttered.''

"Butter is an animal-derived food, Miss Commander, which I never touch.''

"Mr. Hayakawa,'' asked Grimes, ''do you hear anything further from the strange ship?''

"No, Captain. The block has been reestablished.''.

"Let me know when you do hear anything more.'' He punched buttons, then spoke again into the instrument. ''Captain here, Mr. Timmins. Mr. Hayakawa has reported a vessel in our vicinity, apparently heading for Morrowvia. Have *you* picked anything up?''

"Just the normal commercial traffic, sir. A Shaara freighter, *Mmoorroomm*, Rob Roy to ZZrreemm. *Empress of Scotia*, Dunedin to Darnstadt. *Cutty Sark*, Carinthia to Lorn. *Schnauzer*, Siluria to Macbeth. And, according to Sector Plot, the following ships not fitted with Carlotti equipment: *Sundowner*, Aquarius to Faraway, *Rim Eland*, Elsinore to Ultimo. . . ."

"Thank you." Then, speaking more to himself than to anybody else, "*Schnauzer* . . . Dog Star Line . . . cleared for Macbeth. . . . She might finish up there eventually. . . ."

He ignored Maggie's questioning look and went to his playmaster. As its name implied, the device provided entertainment, visual and audio—but this one, a standard fitting in the captain's quarters in all FSS ships, was also hooked up to the vessel's encyclopedia bank. "Get me Lloyd's Register," he ordered. "I want details on *Schnauzer*. Sirian ownership. Dog Star Line. . . ."

The screen lit up, displaying the facsimile of a printed page.

Schnauzer–a new ship, small, exceptionally fast for a merchantman, defensively armed. (The Dog Star Line had long insisted that its vessels were capable of conducting their own defense on some of the trade routes where piracy still persisted.)

"Mphm," he grunted. Back at the telephone he ordered Timmins to send a coded message to the FSS agent at Port Llangowan, on Siluria, to ask the names of *Schnauzer*'s personnel when she cleared outward.

He strongly suspected that the master would be Captain Danzellan.

5

"Master, Roger Danzellan," the Federation's man on Siluria replied eventually. "First mate, Oscar Eklund. Second mate, Francis Delamere. Third mate, Kathryn Daley. Chief engineer, Mannschenn Drive, Evan Jones. Chief engineer Interplanetary Drives, Ian Mackay. Juniors, H. Smith, B. Ostrog, H. Singh. Purser/catering officer, Glynis Trent . . ." The message went on to say that Captain Danzellan and Mr. Delamere had both been among *Corgi*'s complement when she had last been at Port Llangowan. The last piece of information that it contained was that Francis Delamere was the nephew of the Dog Star Line's general manager.

So, obviously, the Dog Star people were interested in Morrowvia. On receiving the report from *Corgi*'s master they had acted, and fast. A suitable ship had been shunted off her doubtlessly well-worn tramlines, and Danzellan had been transferred to her command. Probably he had not wished to have Delamere as one of his officers—but Delamere had pull. Nepotism, as Grimes well knew, existed in the Survey Service. In a privately owned shipping company the climate would be even more suitable to its flourishing.

There was only one thing for Grimes to do—to pile on the Gs and the lumes, to get to Morrowvia before Danzellan. Fortunately, the merchant vessel was not fitted with a Mass Proximity Indicator—the Dog Star Line viewed new navigational aids with suspicion and never fitted them to its ships until their value was well proven. Sooner or later—sooner, Grimes hoped—*Seeker* would pick up *Schnauzer* in her screen and, shortly thereafter, would be able accurately to extrapolate her trajectory. *Schnauzer* would know nothing of *Seeker*'s whereabouts or presence.

And Drongo Kane in his *Southerly Buster?* A coded request for information to the Bug Queen brought the news that he had lifted from Port Fortinbras, his refit completed, with a General Clearance. Such clearances were rarely issued. This one must have cost Kane plenty.

Grimes was spending more and more time in his control room. There was nothing that he could *do*—but he wanted to be on hand when *Schnauzer* was picked up. At last she was there—or *something* was there—and almost infinitesimal spark in the screen, at extreme range. Grimes watched, concealing his impatience, while his navigator, hunched over the big globe of utter darkness, delicately manipulated the controls set into the base of the screen. Slowly a glowing filament was extruded from the center of the sphere—*Seeker*'s track. And then, from that barely visible spark just within the screen's limits, another filament was extended.

"Mphm," grunted Grimes.

The display was informative. Relatively speaking, *Schnauzer* was on *Seeker*'s port beam, a little ahead of the beam actually, and steering a converging course. Morrowvia was out of range of the M.P.I., but there was little doubt that both ships were headed for the same destination.

"Have you an estimate of her speed yet, Mr. Pitcher?" asked Grimes.

"Only a rough one, sir," replied the tall, thin, almost white-haired young man. "Give me an hour, and . . ."

"Extrapolate now, if you will."

"Very good, sir."

"Two beads of light appeared, one on each filament. "Twenty-four hours," said Pitcher. The range had closed slightly but the relative bearing was almost unaltered. "Forty-eight hours." The bearing *was changing*. Seventy-two hours." *Schnauzer* was slightly, very slightly, abaft *Seeker*'s beam. "Ninety-six hours." There was no doubt about it. At the moment *Seeker* had the heels of the Dog Star ship.

Grimes was relieved. He did not want to drive his ship any faster. An almost continuous sense of *déjà vu* is an uncanny thing to have to live with. The temporal precession field had not yet reached a dangerous intensity, but it had been increased to a highly uncomfortable one. Already there was a certain confusion when orders were given and received. Had they been made? Had they been acted upon?

Grimes waited for Pitcher to answer his question, then realized that he had not yet asked it. "Assuming," he said, "that your first estimate of *Schnauzer*'s speed is correct, how much time do we have on Morrowvia before she arrives?"

"Sixty hours Standard, sir. Almost exactly two Morrowvian days."

Not long, thought Grimes. Not long at all for what he had to do. And not knowing what he had to do didn't help matters. He'd just have to make up the rules as he went along.

He said, "We'll maintain a continuous watch on the M.P.I. from now on. Let me know at once if there's any change in the situation, and if any more targets appear on the screen."

"Drongo Kane?" asked Saul.

"Yes, Mr. Saul. Drongo Kane."

The first lieutenant's eyes and teeth were very white in his black face as he smiled mirthlessly. He said, his deep voice little more than a whisper, "I hope that Drongo Kane *is* bound for Morrowvia, Captain."

"Why, Mr. Saul?" Grimes essayed a feeble jest. "Two's company, three's a crowd."

"Racial hatreds die very hard, Captain. To my people, for many, many years, 'slaver' has been an especially dirty word. Ganda, as you know, was colonized by my people. . . . And some hundreds of them, rescued by Kane's *Southerly Buster* before their sun went nova, were sold by him to the Duke of Waldegren. . . ."

"As I said before," Grimes told him, "they

weren't *sold*. They entered the duke's service as indentured labor."

"Even so, sir, I would like to meet Captain Drongo Kane."

"It's just as well," said Grimes, "that he's not a reincarnation of Oliver Cromwell—if he were, Mr. Connery would be after his blood too. . . ."

He regarded his first lieutenant dubiously. He was a good man, a good officer, and Grimes liked him personally. But if *Southerly Buster* made a landing on Morrowvia he would have to be watched carefully. And—who would watch the watchman? Grimes knew that if he wished to reach flag rank in the Service he would have to curb his propensity for taking sides.

"Mphm," he grunted. Then, "I'll leave Control in your capable hands, Mr. Saul. And keep a watchful eye on the M.P.I., Mr. Pitcher. I'm going down to have a few words with Hayakawa."

Lieutenant Hayakawa was on watch—but a psionic communications officer, as any one such will tell you, is *always* on watch. He was not, however, wearing the rig of the day. His grossly obese body was inadequately covered by a short kimono, gray silk with an embroidered design of improbable looking flowers. Scrolls, beautifully inscribed with Japanese ideographs, hung on the bulkheads, although space had been left for a single hologram, a picture of a strikingly symmetrical snow-capped mountain sharp against a blue sky. The deck was covered with a synthetic straw matting. In the air

29

was the faint, sweet pungency of a burning joss stick.

Hayakawa got slowly and ponderously to his feet. "Captain san . . ." he murmured.

"Sit down, Mr. Hayakawa," ordered Grimes. The acceleration—now more than two Gs—was bad enough for him; it would be far, far worse for one of the telepath's build. He lowered himself to a pile of silk cushions. Not for the first time he regretted that Hayakawa had been allowed to break the regulations governing the furnishing of officers' cabins—but PCOs, trading upon their rarity, are privileged persons aboard any ship.

He settled down into a position approximating comfort—and then had to get up and shift the cushions and himself to another site. From the first one he had far too good a view of Hayakawa's psionic amplifier, the disembodied dog's brain suspended in its globe of cloudy nutrient fluid. The view of Mount Fujiyama was much more preferable.

He said, "We have *Schnauzer* on the M.P.I. now."

"I know, Captain."

"You would," remarked Grimes, but without rancor. "And you still haven't picked up any further . . . emanations from her?"

"No. Her PCO is Delwyn Hume. I have met him. He is a good man. What you called my judo technique worked just once with him. It will never work again." Then Hayakawa smiled fatly and sweetly. "But I have other news for you."

"Tell."

"*Southerly Buster*, Captain. Myra Bracegirdle is

the CPO. *She* is good—but, of course, we are all good. Her screen is as tight as that maintained by Hume or myself. But . . .

"She is emotional. During moments of stress her own thoughts seep through. She hates the *Buster*'s mate. His name is Aloysius Dreebly. Now and again—often, in fact—he tries to force his attentions on her."

"Interesting," commented Grimes. He thought, *This is building up to one of those situations where everybody hates everybody. Mr. Saul hates Captain Kane, although he's never met him personally. Myra hates Aloysius. The way Maggie's been carrying on lately I'm beginning to think that she hates me. And I doubt very much if Captain Danzellan feels any great affection for Mr. Francis Delamere. . . . He grinned. But Frankie loves Tabbie. . . .*

He said, "And is *Southerly Buster* bound for Morrowvia?"

"I cannot say, Captain. But she is around. And just before you came in I 'heard' Myra Bracegirdle think, 'Thank the gods there're only seven more days to go before we arrive!' "

And that, Grimes told himself, *means that she gets there at the same time as us. . . .*

He clambered laboriously to his feet, went to Hayakawa's telephone. He punched, first of all, for Lieutenant Connery's quarters, but the engineering officer was not there. He called the engine room, and found him.

"Captain here, Chief. Can you squeeze out another half lume?"

"I can't." Connery's voice was sharp. "The governor's playing up, an' we're havin' to run the Drive on manual control. If I try to push her any more we'll finish up last Thursday in the middle of sweet fuck all!''

"Can't you fix the governor?"

"Not without stoppin' her an' shuttin' down. If you want to carry on, it'll have to wait until we get to Morrowvia."

"Carry on the way you're doing," said Grimes.

6

Seeker saw nothing at all of *Southerly Buster* until both vessels were in orbit about Morrowvia, just prior to landing. This was not surprising, as Drongo Kane's ship had been approaching the planet from the Shakesperian Sector, whilst Grimes had been coming in from Lindisfarne. The angle subtended by these points of origin was little short of 180°. Furthermore, once Morrowvia itself had come within MPI range the instrument, insofar as bodies of less than planetary mass were concerned, was practically useless. And radar had been useless until the shutting down of the time/space twisting interstellar drive.

There was *Seeker*, hanging in equatorial orbit three hundred miles up from the surface, and below her was Morrowvia, an Earth-type world, but unspoiled. There were blue seas and vast expanses of green prairie and forest land, yellow deserts and polar icecaps as dazzlingly white as the drifting cloud masses. There were snow-peaked mountain ranges, and long, winding rivers, on the banks of which, sparsely scattered, were what seemed to be towns and villages—but from a range of hundreds of miles, even with excellent telescopes, human habitations can look like natural formations, and natural formations like buildings, and telltale industrial smog was altogether lacking.

On the night hemisphere the evidence was more conclusive. There were clusters of lights, faint and yellowish. Said Grimes, "Where there's light there's life, intelligent life. . . ."

"Not necessarily," Maggie Lazenby told him. "There are such things as volcanoes, you know. . . ."

"On this hemisphere only? Come off it, Maggie."

"*And* there are such things as luminescent living organisms."

"So what we're seeing are glowworm colonies? And what about the reports from our agents on Siluria and Elsinore and Drroomoorr? Would either the Dog Star Line or Drongo Kane be interested in glowworms?"

"They might be," she said. "They might be."

"Yeah?"

"Yeah. It's high time, Commander Grimes, that you cured yourself of your habit of jumping to conclusions, that you adopted a scientific approach. . . ."

Grimes decided against making some cutting retort. The other officers in the control room were looking far too amused by the exchange. He grunted, then demanded of Lieutenant Saul, "Any sign yet of *Southerly Buster*, Number One?"

"No, sir. Perhaps Mr. Hayakawa . . ."

"I've already asked him. As far as his Peke's brain in aspic and he are concerned, the *Buster*'s maintaining absolute psionic silence."

"*Peke*'s brain?" asked Maggie.

"Can *you* think of any definitely *Japanese* dog at a second's notice?"

And then a voice came from the NST transceiver. It was a man's voice, harsh, yet not unpleasant, strongly accented. "*Southerly Buster* to Aero-Space Control. *Southerly Buster* to Aero-Space Control. Do you read me? Over."

"But there's not any Aero-Space Control here," announced Lieutenant Timmins. "We've already found that out."

"Kane knows that as well as we do," Grimes told him. "But, to judge by his record, he always maintains a facade of absolute legality in everything he does. This fits in."

"And I suppose," said Saul, "that he's already tried to establish communication with the local telepaths, if any, just as we did."

"Not necessarily. His PCO will have 'heard' our Mr. Hayakawa doing just that, and she'll have learned that Morrowvia is lousy with telepaths, but none of them trained. . . . Oh, they *know* we're here, in a vague sort of way. . . ."

"*Southerly Buster* to Aero-Space Control. *Southerly Buster* to Aero-Space Control. Do you read me? Over."

"There she is!" shouted Pitcher suddenly.

There she was, in the radar screen, a tiny yet bright blip. There she was, a new star lifting above the dark limb of the planet, a tiny planetoid reflecting the rays of Gamma Argo.

"If we can see her, she can see us," commented Grimes. He went to the transceiver, ordered, "Put me on to him, Mr. Timmins." He said sternly, "FSS *Seeker* to *Southerly Buster*. FSS *Seeker* to *Southerly Buster*. Come in, please, on audio-visual."

"Comin' in, *Seeker*, comin' in . . ." drawled the voice. There was a swirl of light and color in the little screen, coalescing into a clear picture. Grimes and his officers looked into a control room not unlike their own—even to a weapons control console situated as it would have been in the nerve center of a warship. And this *Southerly Buster* was a merchantman. . . . Drongo Kane calmly regarded Grimes from the screen—bleak yet not altogether humorless blue eyes under a thatch of straw colored hair, in a face that looked as though at some time it had been completely smashed and then reassembled not overcarefully. He said, "I see you, *Seeker*. Can you see me?"

"I see you," snapped Grimes.

"Identify yourself, please, *Seeker*. Can't be too careful once you're off the beaten tracks, y'know."

"Grimes," said the owner of that name at last. "Lieutenant Commander in command of FSS *Seeker*, Survey Vessel."

"Pleased to meet you, Commander Grimes. An' what, may I ask, brings you out to this neck o' the woods?"

"You mayn't ask. That's Federation business, Captain Kane."

The pale eyebrows lifted in mock surprise. "So you know me, Commander! Well, well. Such is fame."

"Or notoriety . . ." murmured Maggie Lazenby.

"Did I hear the lady behind you say somethin'?" inquired Kane.

Grimes ignored this. "What are your intentions, Captain Kane?" he demanded.

"Well, now, that all depends, Commander Grimes. Nobody owns this world 'cepting its people. I've asked if I could make a landing, but got no reply. I s'pose you heard me. But nobody's told me *not* to land. . . ."

"What are your intentions?" demanded Grimes again.

"Oh, to set the old *Buster*'s arse down onto somethin' safe an' solid. An' after that . . . Fossick around. See what we can buy or barter that's worth liftin'. There're some spacemen, Commander—an' I'm one of 'em—who have to *earn* their livin's. . . ."

"It is my duty—and the way that I earn *my* living—to afford protection to all Federation citizens in deep space, interplanetary space, in planetary atmospheres and on planetary surfaces," said Grimes, with deliberate pomposity.

"You needn't put yourself out, Commander."

"I insist, Captain. After all, as *you* said, one can't be too careful when off the beaten track."

Kane's lips moved. Grimes was no lip-reader, but he would have been willing to bet a month's salary that grave doubts were being cast upon his legitimacy—and, were this a less tolerant day and age, his morals. "Suit yourself," said Kane aloud. "But you're only wastin' your time."

"I'm the best judge of that."

"Suit yourself," growled Kane again.

Meanwhile, *Seeker*'s inertial drive had stammered into life and the ship was both slowing and lifting under the application of thrust, being driven into a powered, unnatural orbit so that *Southerly Buster* could pass beneath her.

"I thought you'd be landing first," complained Kane.

"After *you*, Captain," Grimes told him politely.

And just where would Kane be setting his ship down? If *Seeker* had arrived by herself Grimes would have adhered to orthodox Survey Service practice—a dawn landing at the terminator, with the full period of daylight for the initial exploration. And should it be considered safe to establish contact with the indigenes at once, a landing near to an obvious center of population.

Kane had never been an officer in the Survey Service, but he had done his share of exploring, had made first landings on planets upon which he had been the first man to set foot. Slowly, steadily *Southerly Buster* dropped through the atmosphere, with *Seeker* following a respectable distance astern. All *Seeker*'s armament was ready for instant use; Grimes had no doubt that the other ship was in a similar state of readiness. *Corgi*'s people had been hospitably treated on Morrowvia—but this was a large planet, probably divided among tribes or nations. Even though all its populace shared a common origin there had been time for divergence, for the generation of hostilities.

Down dropped *Southerly Buster*–down, down. Down dropped *Seeker*, her people alert for hostile action either from the ground or from the other ship. Grimes let Saul handle the pilotage; this was one of those occasions on which the captain needed to be able to look all ways at once.

Down dropped the two ships—down, down through the clear morning air. Kane's objective was becoming obvious—an expanse of level ground, clear of trees, that was almost an island, bounded to north, west and south by a winding river, to the east by a wooded hill. To north and west of it were villages, each with a sparse sprinkling of yellow lights still visible in the dawn twilight. It was the sort of landing place that Grimes would have selected for himself.

Then the viewscreen, with its high magnification, was no longer necessary, and the big binoculars on their universal mounting were no longer required. And the sun was up, at ground level, casting long shadows, pointing out all the irregularities that could make the landing of a starship hazardous.

Kane was down first, setting the *Buster* neatly into the middle of a patch of green that, from the air at least, looked perfectly smooth. Saul looked up briefly from his controls to Grimes, complaining. "The bastard's picked the best place. . . ."

"To the west of him . . ." Grimes said. "Almost

on the river bank. . . . It doesn't look too bad.
. . .''

"It'll have to do, Captain," murmured the first lieutenant resignedly.

It had to do—and, as Grimes had said, it wasn't too bad.

Only one recoil cylinder in the tripedal landing gear was burst when *Seeker* touched the ground, and there was no other damage.

7

This was not the occasion for full dress uniforms, with fore-and-aft hat, decorations, ceremonial sword and all the other trimmings. This was an occasion for comfortable shorts-and-shirt, with heavy boots and functional sidearms.

So attired, Grimes marched down *Seeker*'s ramp, followed by Captain Philby, the Marine officer, and a squad of his space soldiers. Maggie Lazenby and the other scientists had wished to accompany him, but he had issued strict orders that nobody excepting himself and the Marines was to leave the ship until such time as the situation had been clarified. And this clarification depended upon the local inhabitants as well as upon Drongo Kane. Meanwhile, Grimes had said, no foolish risks were to be taken.

As he marched toward the towering hulk of *Southerly Buster* he regretted his decision to land to the west of that ship; he had put himself at a disadvantage. The light of the still-low sun was blinding, making it difficult for his men and him to avoid the lavish scattering of quartzite boulders that protruded through the short, coarse grass. And it made it impossible to see if Drongo Kane had any weapons aimed at him and his party. Probably he had—but *Seeker's* main armament was trained upon Kane's ship and ready to blow her off the face of the planet at the slightest provocation.

It was a little better once he and the Marines were in the shadow of the other ship. Grimes's eyes adjusted themselves and he stared upward at the blunt, metallic spire as he walked toward it. *Defensively armed!* he thought scornfully. Those two famous quick-firing cannon reported by the Bug Queen were merely an addition to what the *Buster* already had. Even so, in terms of laser and missiles, *Seeker* had the edge on her.

Southerly Buster's ramp was down. At the foot of it an officer was standing, a skeletal figure attired in gray coveralls with shoulder-boards carrying first mate's braid. The man was capless, and bald, and the wrinkled skin of his face was yellow, almost matching the long teeth that he showed when he smiled at the men from *Seeker*.

"Commander Grimes?" he asked in an overly ingratiating voice.

"Mr. Dreebly?" countered Grimes.

"Aloysius Dreebly, sir, at your service."

And so this, thought Grimes, was Aloysius Dreebly. Small wonder that Myra Bracegirdle, *Southerly Buster's* PCO, hated him. He matched his name—as people with ugly names so very often do. They, as it were, grow to fit the labels that misguided parents bestow upon them at birth. *And this Dreebly,* Grimes continued thinking, *I wouldn't trust him behind me. He'd either kiss my arse or stab me in the back—or both.*

"And will you come aboard, Commander? Captain Kane is waiting for you."

"Certainly, Mr. Dreebly. Lead the way, please."

"Oh, sir, I'm afraid I cannot allow these other men aboard the ship. . . ."

"And I'm afraid that I can't board unless I have an escort of my own people. Captain Philby!"

"Sir!"

The young Marine officer had his pistol out, pointing at Dreebly. His sergeant and the six privates held their rifles at the ready.

"But, sir . . . what are you thinking of? This is *piracy!*"

"Hardly, Mr. Dreebly. All the way from our ship to yours we were tracked by the muzzle of one of your quick-firers. Surely you will allow us to show *our* teeth."

"Let the bastards aboard, Dreebly!" boomed Kane's voice from a loudspeaker. "But put your guns away first, Commander. I don't expect my guests to check in their pocket artillery at the door—but, on the other hand, I take a dim view if it's waved in my face."

At a word from Grimes Philby reholstered his pistol, the Marines slung their machine rifles. Dreebly shambled up the ramp to the after airlock, followed by the party from *Seeker*. Inside the compartment, Grimes looked about him curiously. He had been expecting something squalid—but, at first glance at least, this seemed to be a reasonably well-kept ship. There was a distinct absence of Survey Service spit-and-polish—but such is found only in vessels where there is a superfluity of ratings to do

the spitting and polishing. There was shabbiness—
but everything looked to be in excellent working
order.

The elevator from the stern to the control room
would accommodate only four men. Grimes decided
to take Philby and one private with him, told the
captain to tell his sergeant and the remaining
Marines to stand guard in the airlock and at the foot
of the ramp. (The Marines were apt to sulk if anybody but one of their own officers gave them a direct
order.) Dreebly led the way into the cage and, as
soon as the others were standing there with him,
pressed a button.

She was quite a hunk of ship, this *Southerly Buster*, thought Grimes, as they slid rapidly upward,
deck after deck. She had probably started life as an
Interstellar Transport Commission's *Gamma Class*
cargo liner but, under successive ownership, had
been modified and remodified many times. A vessel
this size, even with a minimal crew, would be
expensive to run. Whatever Kane's activities were,
they must show a profit.

The cage came to a gentle halt. *"This* way,
please, gentlemen,'' said Dreebly. He led the way
into a short alleyway, to a door with a sign, Captain,
written above it. The door opened, admitting them
into a spacious day cabin. Drongo Kane rose from an
easy chair to greet them, but did not offer to shake
hands.

He was as tall as his lanky bean pole of a mate, but
there was a little more flesh on his bones. He moved
with a decisive sort of grace, like an efficient hunting
animal. He wasted no time on courtesies.

"Well, Commander Grimes?" he demanded.

"Captain Kane, I thought that we might combine forces. . . ."

"Did you, now? You've very kindly seen me down to the surface in one piece—not that I needed you—an' now you can go and play soldiers off by yourself, somewhere."

Grimes's prominent ears flamed. He was aware that Captain Philby and the Marine were looking at him, were thinking, *What's the old man going to say (or do) now?* Well, what *was* the old man (Grimes) going to say (or do) now?

He said, "I represent the Federation, Captain."

"An' this planet, Commander, is not a Federated World."

"Yet," said Grimes.

"If ever," said Kane.

"I was sent here by the Federation . . ." Grimes began again.

"To claim this planet—possibly against the wishes of its people?"

"To conduct a survey."

"Then conduct your survey. I'm not stoppin' you."

"But I'm responsible for your safety, and that of your ship, Captain. You're a citizen of Austral, a Federated World, and your vessel's port of registry is Port Southern, on that planet."

"I don't need any snotty nosed Space Scouts to see me across the road."

"Maybe you don't, Captain Kane—but you're here, and I'm here, and I am obliged to carry out my duties to the best of my ability."

"Cor stiffen the bleedin' crows!" swore Kane disgustedly. Then, to somebody who had come in silently and was standing behind Grimes, "Yes, Myra?"

Grimes turned. So this was the Myra Bracegirdle of whom Hayakawa had talked. She was a tall girl, but thin rather than slender (this *Southerly Buster* must be a poor feeding ship), her face with its too prominent bones, too wide mouth and too big, dark eyes framed by silky blonde hair.

She said, "A word with you, Captain. Alone."

"Oh, don't worry about the Space Scouts, Myra. They're here to look after us. We have no secrets from *them*."

"*They* are on the way here, Captain. They saw the ships land. They have heard about spaceships, of course, but have never seen one. . . ."

And what about Corgi? Grimes asked himself. *But she could have landed on the other side of the world from here.*

He said, "Captain Kane, do you mind if I call my ship?"

"Go ahead, Commander. This is Liberty Hall; you can spit on the mat and call the cat a bastard."

But as Grimes was raising his wrist transceiver to his mouth it buzzed sharply, then Saul's voice issued from the little instrument. "First lieutenant here, Captain. Mr. Hayakawa reports that parties of natives are approaching the landing site from both villages."

"I'll be right back," said Grimes.

"Don't let me keep you," said Kane. "Mr. Dreebly, please show these gentlemen off the premises."

"Oh, Captain," Grimes said, pausing in the doorway, "I shall take a very dim view if you act in a hostile manner toward the natives."

"And what if they act in a hostile manner toward me?"

"That," said Grimes, "will be different."

8

Grimes did not hurry back to his own ship, neither did he dawdle. He would have liked to have hurried, but was aware that Kane would be watching him. He walked at a moderately brisk pace, with Philby at his side and the other Marines marching after them.

"Sir," asked Philby, "do you think they'll be hostile?"

"*Corgi*'s crew didn't find them so, Captain Philby. But she landed on another part of the planet, among different people. We'll just have to play it by ear. . . ."

"A show of force . . ." murmured the young officer, as though he were looking forward to it.

And he was, thought Grimes. He was. He glanced at Philby's face—young, unlined, features, save for the strong chin, indeterminate. A Marine Corps recruiting poster face. . . . There was no vice in it—neither was there any sensitivity or imagination. It was the face of a man who could have written those famous lines—and without ironical intention:

> Whatever happens, we have got
> The Maxim gun—and they have not.

"Don't forget," said Grimes, "that this is *their* world, and that we're interlopers."

"Yes, sir, but we're civilized. Aren't we?"

"Mphm."

"And these people, out of the mainstream for so long, need to be taught the Federation's way of life. . . ."

Was Philby joking? No, Grimes decided, he was not. He said mildly, "The Federation's way of life as exemplified by whom? By the crew of *Seeker?* By Captain Drongo Kane and *his* crew? Or by Captain Danzellan and *Corgi*'s or *Schnauzer*'s people? Kane and Danzellan are Federation citizens, just as we are."

"Yes, sir. I suppose so. But . . ."

"But we have the superior fire power. Not all that superior. From what we saw aboard *Southerly Buster* I'd say she packs the wallop of a young battleship. And I should imagine that *Schnauzer* could show her teeth if she had to."

"What are your orders, sir?" asked Philby stiffly, obviously regretting having initiated the conversation.

"Just keep handy while I meet the natives. Better call another half dozen of your men down. Have your weapons ready—but not too obviously."

"With your permission, sir." Philby raised his wrist transceiver to his mouth. "Mr. Saul? Captain Philby here. Would you mind telling Corporal Smithers to detail six men for EVA? Yes, number three battle equipment. Over."

Then Grimes gave his orders. "Mr. Saul, Captain here. Do as Captain Philby says. And ask Dr. Lazenby if she'll join me at the after airlock. Yes. At once. All other officers and all ratings, with the exception of the six Marines, to remain on board. Yes, main and secondary armament to remain in a condition of readiness.''

He heard the sergeant, who was a pace or two behind him, whisper something to one of the Marines about a show of force. He smiled to himself. He was not showing the force at his disposal—but it was nice to know that it was handy.

He beckoned Maggie down from the open airlock door. She walked gracefully down the ramp, despite the fact that she was hung around with all manner of equipment—cameras, recorders, even a sketch block and stylus.

She said, "We've had a good look at them through the control room telescope and binoculars. They seem to be human. . . ."

"Are they armed?"

"Some are carrying spears, and a few have longbows. . . ."

The additional Marines clattered down the ramp. Grimes looked at the automatic weapons they carried and hoped that they would not be used. He was pleased to see that each man had a couple of sleep gas grenades at his belt, and that one of them was carrying extra respirators; these he handed out to Grimes, Philby and to the other members of the party that had gone to *Southerly Buster*.

There was activity just by the boarding ramp of that ship, too. Grimes borrowed Maggie's binoculars, saw that Kane, Dreebly and three more men had come outside and that a folding table had been set up. The wares spread upon it glittered in the strong sunlight. Trade goods, Grimes decided. Bright, pretty baubles. . . . And did he hope to buy a territory, a continent, a planet, even, for a string of glass beads? Why not? Things as strange had happened in Man's long history.

The first of the party of natives, that from the north, was now in sight from ground level. They moved with catlike smoothness over the grass, threading their way around the outcropping boulders. There were twenty of them—ten males and ten females. *Ten men and ten women*, Grimes corrected himself. Six men, carrying long spears, were in the lead, advancing in open order. Then came the women, eight of whom carried bows and who had quivers of arrows slung over their shoulders. This appeared to be their only clothing. The remaining four men brought up the rear.

Humans, thought Grimes, studying them through Maggie's glasses. Exceptionally handsome humans. That all of them were unclothed was no indication of their cultural level—naturism was the rule rather than the exception on several highly civilized planets, such as Arcadia. Their skins varied in color from pale gold to a dark brown, the hair of their heads and their body hair—which was normally distributed—was of a variety of colors, black, white, gray, brown, a coppery gold. . . . Grimes focused his attention on a girl. The short hair of her head was particolored, stripes of darker and lighter gray alternating. The effect was odd, but not unpleasing. He grunted. There was something odd about her eyes, too. But this offshoot of humanity, cut off from the main stem for generations, must have tended to grow apart from the generality of humankind.

The natives came to a halt by *Southerly Buster*'s ramp. The men stood aside to let two of the women, the two who carried no weapons, advance slowly to where Drongo Kane was standing by his table of trade goods. These two women were a little taller, a little larger than their companions, but no less graceful. They wore an air of maturity, but they were no less beautiful. They were talking to Kane and he seemed to be having no trouble understanding them, and they seemed to be having no trouble in understanding him.

"Here they come, sir," said Philby. "*Our* lot."

Grimes lowered the glasses, turned to face the visitors. This was a smaller party, only six people. Once again there was an equal division of the sexes.

Their leader, flanked by a spearman on either side of her, advanced slowly to where Grimes, with Maggie Lazenby beside him, was standing. Grimes saluted with a flourish—and a part of his mind stood back and laughed wryly at his according this courtesy to a naked savage. But a savage she was not. Savages tend to be dirty, unkempt; she was fastidiously clean. Her short hair was snowy, gleaming white, her lustrous skin was brown, the lips of her generous mouth a red that seemed natural rather than the result of applied cosmetics. The overall effect was definitely erotic. Grimes heard one of the Marines whistle, heard another whisper, "Buy that one for me, Daddy. . . ." He could not blame either of them—but felt definitely censorious when

Magie murmured, "And you can buy either—or both—of her boyfriends for me. . . ."

The two men were tall. Both were golden skinned; one had orange-colored hair, the other was black-haired. Of their essential maleness there was no doubt. Each, however, was built more on the lines of an Apollo than a Hercules, and each moved with a fluid grace as pronounced as that with which the woman walked.

To her, not at all reluctantly, Grimes returned his attention. He knew that the slow inspection that he was making was not mannerly, but he could not help himself. He told himself that it was his duty, as captain of a survey ship, to make such an inspection. Her eyes, he saw, were a peculiar greenish-yellow, and the tips of her ears were pointed. Her cheekbones were prominent, more so than the firm chin. His regard shifted slowly downward. Beneath each full but firm breast there was a rudimentary nipple. But she was human, human—even though the bare feet, which should have been long and slender, were oddly chubby.

She was human when she spoke. She said, "Welcome to Morrowvia." The accent was strange (of course) and the timbre of her voice held a quality that was hard to define.

"Thank you," replied Grimes. Then, "And whom do I have the honor of addressing?" The words, he realized as soon as he gave them utterance, were too formal, too far removed from everyday speech. But she understood them. Evidently the vocabulary had not become impoverished during the long years between first settlement and rediscovery.

She said simply, "My name is Maya. I am the queen."

So I'm saved the trouble of saying, "Take me to your leader," Grimes thought smugly. *Drongo must be doing his dickering with some very minor court official.* . . . He asked suavely, "And what is the name of your country, Your Majesty? Is it, too, called Morrowvia?"

Puzzle lines creased her rather broad face. And then she smiled. Her teeth were very white and looked sharp, the teeth of a carnivore rather than of an omnivore. She said, "You do not understand. The captain of the ship called *Corgi* made the same mistake when he landed at Melbourne, many kilometers from here. I have been told that he called the Queen of Melbourne 'Your Majesty.' He explained, later, that this is a title given to queens on your world, or worlds. . . ." She added modestly, yet not without a touch of pride, "I am the elected Queen of Cambridge, the town to the south of where you have landed."

"Melbourne . . ." echoed Grimes. "Cambridge . . ." But it made sense. Homesick colonists have always perpetuated the names of their home towns.

"*He*—Morrow—left us a book, a big book, in which he had written all the names that we are to use for our towns. . . ." Maya went on.

Yes, it made sense all right. It was all too probable that the people of a Lost Colony would deviate from the human norm—but if they still spoke a recognizable major Earth language, and if their centers of population were named after Earth cities, whoever rediscovered them would have no doubt as to their essential humanity.

54

"Then what shall I call you," asked Grimes, "if 'Your Majesty' is not correct?"

"Maya," she told him. "And I shall call you . . ."

"Commander Grimes," he said firmly. It was not that he would at all object to being on given name terms with this rather gorgeous creature—but not in front of his subordinates. "Have you a second name, Maya?" he asked.

"Yes, Commander Grimes. It is Smith."

Maya Smith, thought Grimes, a little wildly. *Maya Smith, the Queen of Cambridge. . . . And not a rag to cover her, not even any Crown Jewels. . . . And escorted by henchmen and henchwomen armed to the teeth with spears and bows and arrows. . . .*

Spears and bows and arrows . . . they could be just as lethal as more sophisticated weaponry. Grimes looked away hastily from the Queen of Cambridge to her people, saw, with relief, that there was no immediate cause for worry. The Morowvians were not using the time-honored technique of enthusiastic fraternization, of close, ostensibly friendly contact that would make the snatching of guns from their owners' hands all too easy when the time came. There was a certain stand-offishness about them, in fact, an avoidance of too close physical proximity. Some of the Marines, to judge by the way that they were looking at the native women, would have wished it otherwise—but Philby and his sergeant were keeping a watchful eye both on their men and on the visitors.

Grimes felt free to continue his conversation with Maya. He gestured toward *Southerly Buster*, where the people from the other village were still clustered about Kane and his officers. "And your friend . . . what is she called?"

"*She* is no friend of mine. That *cat!*"

"But who is she?"

"Her name is Sabrina. She is the Queen of Oxford." The woman turned away from Grimes, stared toward Kane's vessel and the activity around her boarding ramp. She said, in a rather hurt voice, "The other ship has brought gifts for the people. Did you bring no gifts?"

"Mphm," Grimes grunted. He thought, *There must be something in my storerooms that she'd fancy.* . . . He said, "We did not know what you would like. Perhaps you would care to come on board, to take refreshments with us. Then we shall be able to discuss matters."

Maggie Lazenby snorted delicately.

"Thank you, Commander Grimes," said Maya Smith. "And my people?"

"They may come aboard too. But I must request that they leave their weapons outside."

She looked at him in some amazement. "But we never bring weapons into another person's home. They are for hunting, and for defense. There will be nothing to hunt in your ship—and surely we shall not need to defend ourselves against anything!"

You have *been away from the mainstream of civilization a long time!* thought Grimes.

He called the first lieutenant on his wrist transceiver to warn him to prepare to receive guests, then led the way up the ramp, into the ship.

9

The Survey Service has procedures laid down for practically everything, and as long as you stick to them you will not go far wrong. Grimes didn't need to consult the handbook titled *Procedures For Entertaining Alien Potentates*. He had entertained Alien Potentates before. Insofar as the milking of such beings of useful information was concerned he had conformed to the good old principle—candy is dandy, but licker is quicker. Of course, it was at times rather hard to decide what constituted either candy or liquor for some of the more exotic life forms. . . .

The majority of the natives had been shown into the wardroom, there to be entertained by the first lieutenant and—with the exception of Maggie Lazenby—the senior scientific officers. In his own day cabin Grimes had Maya Smith, the two men who constituted her bodyguard, and Maggie. He knew that it was foolish of him to feel ill at ease sitting there, making polite conversation with a naked woman and two naked men. Maggie took the situation for granted, of course—but her upbringing had been different from his. On Arcadia, the planet of her birth and upbringing, clothing was worn only when the weather was cold enough to justify the inconvenience.

"Tea, Maya?" asked Grimes. "Coffee?"

"What is tea?" she asked him. "What is coffee?"

"What do you drink usually?" he asked.

"Water, of course," she told him.

"And on special ocasions?"

"Water."

"Mphm." He got up, opened his liquor cabinet. The light inside it was reflected brightly from the labels of bottles, from polished glasses.

Maya said, "How pretty!"

"Perhaps you would like to try . . . What would you like to try?"

"Angels' Tears," she said.

So she could read as well as speak Anglic. Grimes set out five liqueur glasses on the counter, uncorked the tall, beautifully proportioned bottle and filled them. He handed one to Maya, then served Maggie, then the two men. He lifted the remaining glass, said, "Here's mud in your eye!" and sipped. Maya sipped. The two men sipped. Maya spat like an angry cat. The men looked as though they would have liked to do the same, but they were too overawed by their unfamiliar surroundings.

"Firewater!" ejaculated the Morrowvian woman at last.

Grimes wondered what the distillers on Altairia would think if they could hear their most prized product so denigrated. This liqueur was almost pure alcohol—but it was smooth, smooth, and the cunning blend of spices used for flavoring could never

58

be duplicated off the planet of its origin. Then he remembered a girl he had known on Dunsinane. He had not minded buying her expensive drinks, but he had been shocked by the way in which she misused them. The ending of what promised to be a beautiful friendship had come when she had poured Angels' Tears over a dish of ice cream. . . .

He said, "Perhaps this drink is a little strong to those who are not accustomed to it. But there is a way of making it less . . . fiery." He pressed the button, and in seconds a stewardess was in the cabin. The girl blushed furiously when she saw the nudity of the two Morrowvian men, but she tried hard to ignore their presence.

"Jennifer," said Grimes, "bring three dishes of ice cream."

"What flavor, sir?"

What flavor ice cream had that girl used for her appalling concoction? "Chocolate," said Grimes.

"Very good, sir."

She was not gone long. Grimes took the tray from her when she returned; he was afraid that she might drop it when attempting to serve the naked bodyguards. He set it down on the table, then took Maya's glass from her. He poured the contents over one of the dishes of ice cream, handed it to her. "Now try it," he said.

She ignored the spoon. She raised the dish in her two hands to mouth level. Her pink tongue flickered out. There was a very delicate slurping sound. Then she said to her bodyguards, "Thomas, William— this is *good!*"

"I'm glad you like it," said Grimes, handing

their portions to the two men. Then—"The same again?"

"If I may," replied Maya politely.

Alcohol, even when mixed with ice cream, is a good lubricant of the vocal cords. Maya, after her second helping, became talkative. More than merely talkative . . . she became affectionate. She tended to rub up against Grimes whenever he gave her the opportunity. He would have found her advances far more welcome if Maggie had not been watching amusedly, if the two bodyguards had not been present. Not that the bodyguards seemed to mind what their mistress was doing; were it not for her inhibiting presence they would have behaved toward Maggie Lazenby as she, Maya, was behaving toward Grimes. . . .

"Such a long time . . ." gushed Maya. "Such a long, long time. . . . We knew we came from the stars, in a big ship. . . . Not *us*, of course, but our first fathers and mothers. . . . We hoped that some time some other ship would come from the stars. . . . But it's been a long, long time. . . .

"And then, after the ship called *Corgi* came, we thought that the next ships would land at Melbourne, and that it'd be *years* before we saw one. . . . The Queen of Melbourne, they say, now has a cold box to keep her meat and her water in, and she has books, *new* books, about all sorts of marvelous things. . . . And what are *you* giving *me*, Commander Grimes?"

I know what I'd like to give you, he thought. The close proximity of smooth, warm woman-flesh was putting ideas into his head. He said, trying to keep the conversation under control, "You have books?"

"'Course we have books—but we can't make any new ones. Every town has a copy of The History; it was printed and printed and printed, years ago, when the machines were still working. . . ."

"The History?" asked Grimes.

"Yes. The History. All about Earth, and the first flights away from Earth, and the last voyage of the *Lode Cougar*. . . ."

"The ship that brought you here?"

"Of course. You don't suppose we *walked*, do you?"

"Hardly. But tell me, how do you get about your world? Do you walk, or ride, or fly?"

"There were machines once, for riding and flying, but they wore out. We walk now. Everywhere. The Messengers are the long walkers."

"I suppose that you have to maintain a messenger service for the business of government."

"What business?" She pulled away from Grimes, stood tall and erect. It was a pity that she spoiled the effect by wavering lightly. "What government? *I* am the government."

"But surely," Grimes persisted, "you must have some planetary authority in overall charge. Or national authorities. . . ."

"But why?" she asked. "But why? I look after the affairs of *my* town, Sabrina looks after the affairs of *her* town, and so on. Who can tell me how much meat is to be dried or salted before the onset of winter? Who can tell me how the town's children are to be brought up? *I* am the government, of my own town. What else is needed?"

"It seems to work, this system of theirs . . ." commented Maggie Lazenby.

" 'Course it works. Too many people in one town—then start new town."

"But," persisted Grimes, "there's more to government than mayoral duties—or queenly duties. Public health, for example. . . ."

"Every town has its doctor, to give medicine, set broken bones and so on. . . ."

Grimes looked appealingly at Maggie. She looked back at him, and shrugged. So he plodded on, unassisted. "But you must have a capital city. . . ."

Maya said, "We have. But it does not rule us. We rule ourselves. It is built around the landing place of the *Lode Cougar*. The machines are there, although they have not worked for *years*. There are the records—but all we need to know is in The History. . . ."

"And the name of this city?"

"Ballarat."

So Morrow—presumably he had been master of *Lode Cougar*—was an Australian. There was a Ballarat, on Earth, not far from Port Woomera.

"And how do we get to Ballarat?" asked Grimes.

"It is many, many days' walk. . . ."

"I wasn't thinking of walking."

"The exercise wouldn't do you any harm," Maggie told him.

"In my house there is a map. . . ."

The telephone buzzed sharply. Grimes answered it. Saul's deep voice came from the speaker, "Captain, our orbital spy eyes have reported the arrival of another ship. Mr. Hayakawa says that it is *Schnauzer*."

So—*Schnauzer* had arrived, earlier than expected. Presumably Captain Danzellan's PCO had picked up indications that other vessels were bound for Morrowvia. And presumably he would make his landing in the same location that he had used before, in *Corgi*. Where was it again? Melbourne. Grimes tried to remember his Australian geography. The Ballarat on Earth wasn't far from Melbourne. He hoped that this would also be the case on this planet, so that he could kill two birds with one stone.

Lieutenant Saul could look after the shop in his, Grimes's, absence.

Somebody would have to keep an eye on Drongo Kane.

10

Grimes would have liked to have been able to fly at once to Melbourne, to be there and waiting when *Schnauzer* arrived. But there was so much to be done first—the delegation of authority, the pinnace to be readied and stocked for an absence from the mother ship of indefinite duration and, last but not least, to determine the location of Captain Danzellan's arrival point with accuracy. The orbiting spy eyes would do this, of course—provided that *Schnauzer* was not using some device to render their data erroneous. She was not a warship—but it was safe to assume that she was fitted with electronic equipment not usually found aboard a merchantman.

So, early in the afternoon, Grimes and Maggie Lazenby accompanied Maya and her people back to their town. Fortunately their intake of fortified ice cream had slowed the Morrowvians down, otherwise Grimes would have found it hard to keep up with them. Even so, he was soon sweating in his tropical uniform, and his bare knees were scratched by the long, spiky grass that grew on the bank of the river, and he had managed to twist his right ankle quite painfully shortly after the departure from *Seeker*. . . .

Lethargic though they were, the Morrowvians made good time. Their bare skins, Grimes noted enviously seemed proof against the razor-edged grass blades—or it could be that they, somehow, avoided painful contact. And Maggie, once they were out of sight of the ship, removed her uniform shirt and gave it to Grimes to carry. She was as unself-conscious in her semi-nudity as the natives were in their complete nakedness. Grimes wished that he dare follow her example, but he did not have the advantage of her upbringing.

There was one welcome halt on the way. One of the bow-women called out, and pointed to a swirl that broke the otherwise placid surface of the slow-flowing river. She unhitched a coil of line from the belt that encircled her slim waist, bent the end of it to a viciously barbed arrow. She let fly, the line snaking out behind the missile. When it hit there was a mad, explosive flurry as a creature about half the size of a full grown man leaped clear of the water. Two of the men dropped their spears, grabbed the line by its few remaining coils. Slowly, with odd growling grunts, they hauled it in, playing the aquatic creature like an angler playing a fish, towing it to a stretch of bank where the shore shelved gently to a sandy beach.

Grimes and Maggie watched as the thing was landed—she busy with her camera.

"Salmon," announced Maya. "It is good eating."

" '*Salmon?* thought Grimes. It was like no salmon that he had ever seen. It was, he supposed, some kind of fish, or some kind of ichthyoid, although it looked more like a scaly seal than anything else. But what it was called made sense. Long, long ago somebody—Morrow?—had said, "Give *everything* Earth names—and then, when this world is redis-covered, nobody will doubt that we're an Earth col-ony."

A slash from a vicious looking knife killed the beast, and it was slung from a spear and carried by two of the men. The journey continued.

They reached the town at last. It was a neat as-semblage of low, adobe buildings, well spaced along dirt streets, with trees, each a vivid explosion of emerald foliage and crimson blossom, growing be-tween the houses. Maya's house (palace?) was a little larger than the others, and atop a tall post just outside the main entrance was a gleaming five pointed star, wrought from silvery metal.

There were people in the streets, men, women and children. They were curious, but not obtrusively so. They were remarkably quiet, except for a group of youngsters playing some sort of ball game. These did not even pause in their sport as the queen and her guests passed them.

It was delightfully cool inside Maya's house. The small windows were unglazed, but those facing the sun were screened with matting, cutting out the glare while admitting the breeze. The room into which she took Grimes and Maggie was large, sparsely fur-nished. There was a big, solid table, a half dozen square, sturdy chairs. On one wall was a map of the planet, drawn to Mercatorial projection. The seas were tinted blue, the land masses either green or brown except in the polar regions, where they were white.

Maya walked slowly to this map. Her fingers stabbed at it. "This," she said, "is the River Thames. It flows into the Atlantic Ocean. Here, on this wide bend, is Cambridge. . . ."

"Mphm." *And this Cambridge,* thought Grimes, *is about in the middle of a continent, an island continent that straggles untidily over much of the equatorial belt, called—of all names!—England. . . . And where the hell is Melbourne?* He studied the map closely. There was a North Australia, another island continent, roughly rectangular, in the northern hemisphere. And there was a River Yarra. His right forefinger traced its winding course from the sea, from the Indian Ocean, to the contour lines that marked the foothills of the Dandenongs. Yes, here was Melbourne. And to the north of it, still on the river, was Ballarat.

He aked, "How do your people cross the seas, Maya? You said that all the machines, including the flying machines, had broken down years ago."

"There are machines *and* machines, Commander Grimes. We have the wind, and we have balloons, and we have sailing boats. The balloons can go only with the wind, of course, but the sailing boats—what is the expression?—can beat to windward. . . ." Then she said abruptly, "I am a poor hostess. You must be thirsty. . . ."

Not as thirsty as you *must be,* thought Grimes,

after gorging yourself on that horrid mixture. . . .

"I could use a drink, Maya," said Maggie.

The Morrowvian woman went to the shelved cupboard where pottery, brightly and pleasingly glazed, was stacked. She took out six shallow bowls, set them on the table. Then she took down a stoppered pitcher that was hanging on the wall. This was not glazed, and its porous sides were bedewed with moisture. She poured from this into three of the bowls. The remaining vessels she filled with food from a deep dish that she extracted from the depths of a primitive refrigerator, a large unglazed earthenware box standing in a small bath of water. She used her hands to transfer cubes of white flesh from the dish to the bowls. There was no sign of any knives, forks or spoons.

She lifted her bowl of water to her mouth. She grinned and said "Here's mud in your eye!" She *lapped* the liquid, a little noisily. Grimes and Maggie drank more conventionally. The water was pleasantly cool, had a faint vegetable tang to it. Probably it was safe enough—but, in any case, all of *Seeker*'s people had been given wide spectrum antibiotic shots before landing.

Maya, using one hand only, quite delicately helped herself to food from her bowl. Without hesitation Maggie followed suit. Her fine eyebrows arched in surprised appreciation. Grimes took a cautious sample. This, he decided after the first nibble, was *good*. It reminded him of a dish that he had enjoyed during his last leave on Earth, part of which he had spent in Mexico. This had been fish—

raw, but seasoned, and marinaded in the juice of freshly squeezed limes. He would have liked some more, but it would be a long time, he feared, before he would be able properly to relax and enjoy whatever social amenities this planet afforded.

Maggie, having followed Maya's example in licking her hands clean, had unslung one of her cameras, was pointing it at the map. She explained, "We have to have a copy of this, so that we can find our way to Melbourne."

"It will not be necessary. I can send a Messenger with you. But I warn you, it is a long journey, unless you go in your ship."

"We shall not go in the ship, Maya," Grimes told her. "But we shall not be walking, either. We shall use a pinnace, a relatively small flying boat."

"I have never flown," said Maya wistfully. "Not even in a balloon. Do you think that I . . .?"

"Why not?" said Grimes. *Why not?* he thought. *She'll be able to introduce me to her sister queen in Melbourne.*

"When do we leave?" she asked him.

"In the morning, as soon after sunrise as possible." That would be a good time; Melbourne was only a degree or so west of Cambridge. The flight would be made in daylight, and arrival would be well before sunset.

She said, "You will excuse me. I must make arrangements for my deputy to run affairs during my absence."

"I must do likewise," said Grimes.

They looked at each other gravely, both monarchs

of a small kingdom, both with the cares of state heavy on their shoulders. It was unkind of Maggie to spoil the effect by snickering.

"I shall send an escort with you," said Maya.

"It is not necessary. All we have to do is to follow the river."

"But wolves have been reported along the river bank. . . ."

And if the "wolves" of Morrowvia bore the same relationship to Terran wolves as did the Morrowvian "salmon" to Terran salmon, Grimes didn't want to meet them. He said so to Maya.

So he and Maggie, escorted by four spearmen and two bow-women, walked back to the ship. The members of the escort were too awestricken by the visitors from Outside to talk unless spoken to, and after ten minutes or so of very heavy going no attempt was made at conversation.

11

Grimes did not get much sleep that night.

He did not want to leave his ship until he was reasonably sure that the situation was under control. Drongo Kane was the main problem. Just what were his intentions? *Southerly Buster* had been kept under close observation from *Seeker*, and all the activity around her airlock had been filmed. Highly sensitive long-range microphones had been trained upon her—but Kane had set up some small noise-making machine that produced a continuous *whup, whup, whup.* . . . Hayakawa, disregarding the Rhine Institute code of ethics, had tried to pry, but Myra Bracegirdle, Kane's PCO, was maintaining an unbreakable block over the minds of all the *Buster*'s personnel. He had then tried to pick up the thoughts of the people in the town of Oxford, with little more success.

Grimes studied the film that had been made. He watched, on the screen, Kane talking amicably with Sabrina, the Queen of Oxford. He seemed to be laying on the charm with a trowel, and the Morrowvian woman was lapping it up. She smiled smugly when Drongo hung a scintillating string of synthetic diamonds about her neck, and her chubby hand went up to stroke the huge ruby that formed the pendant of the necklace, that glowed with crimson fire between her ample, golden-skinned breasts. She looked, thought Grimes, like a sleek cat that had got its nose into the cream. If it had not been for that annoying *whup, whup, whup* he would have heard her purring. It was shortly after her acceptance of this gift that Kane took her into the ship. Dreebly and two others—a little, fat man who, to judge by his braid, was the second mate and a cadaverous blonde in catering officer's uniform—remained by the table, handing out cheap jewelry, hand mirrors, pocket knives (a bad guess, thought Grimes amusedly, in this nudist culture), pairs of scissors and (always a sure way of buying goodwill) a quite good selection of children's toys. But it was the books that were in the greatest demand. The lens of one of the cameras that had been used zoomed in to a close-up of the display. Their covers were brightly-colored, eye-catching. They were, every one of them, handouts from the Tourist Bureaus of the more glamorous worlds of the galaxy.

Did Kane intend opening a travel agency on this world? It was possible, Grimes conceded. After all, the man was a shipowner. And his ship, according to the report from Elsinore, had been modified to suit her for the carriage of passengers.

"I don't like the looks of this, Captain," said the first lieutenant.

"What don't you like about it, Mr. Saul?" asked Grimes.

"I still remember what he did on Ganda."

"He can hardly do the same here. These people aren't being evacuated from their world before it's destroyed. They're quite happy here. In any case, the Gandans were skilled workmen, technicians. These people, so far as I can see, are little better than savages. *Nice* savages, I admit, but . . ."

"Forgive me for saying so, Captain, but you're very simple, aren't you?"

Grimes's prominent ears reddened. He demanded sharply, "What do you mean, Mr. Saul?"

"You've seen even more of these people than I have, sir. Have you seen an ugly man or woman?"

"No," admitted Grimes.

"And there are worlds where beautiful women are in great demand. . . ."

"And there are the quite stringent laws prohibiting the traffic in human merchandise," said Grimes.

"Kane is bound to find some loophole," insisted Saul. "Just as he did on Ganda." Then his racial bitterness found utterance. "After all, he's a *white* man."

Grimes sighed. He wished, as he had wished before, that Saul would forget the color of his skin. He said tiredly, "All right, all right—Whitey's to blame for *everything*. But, from my reading of history, I seem to remember that it was the fat black kings on the west coast of Africa who sold their own people to the white slave traders. . . ."

"Just as that fat yellow queen whom Kane entertained will sell her people to the white slave trader."

"I wouldn't call her *fat* . . ." objected Grimes, trying to bring the conversation to a lighter level.

"Just pleasantly plump, dearie," said Maggie Lazenby. "But, as you say, Drongo won't be able to pull off a coup like the Gandan effort twice running. And even if he makes a deal with some non-Federated world, *he's* still a Federation citizen and subject to Federation law."

"Yes, Commander Lazenby," agreed Saul dubiously. "But I don't trust him."

"Who does?" said Grimes. "During my absence you'll just have to watch him, Mr. Saul, like a cat watching a mouse." He added, "Like a black cat watching a white mouse."

"A white rat, you mean," grumbled Saul.

12

Before sunrise the pinnace was ready.

Grimes was taking with him Pitcher, the navigator, Ensign Billard who, as well as being assistant communications officer (electronic), was a qualified atmosphere pilot, and Commander Maggie Lazenby. All of them carried sidearms. The pinnace, too, was armed, being fitted with a laser cannon and two 20 mm machine guns.

Just as the sun was coming up, Grimes, Pitcher, Billard and Maggie stood outside the ship, watching as the small craft, its inertial drive muttering irritably, was eased out of its bay high on the ship's side, maneuvered down to the ground. It landed rather clumsily. Saul stepped out of the pilot's cabin and saluted with rather less than his usual snap. (He had been up, working, all night.) He said, "She's all yours, Captain."

"Thank you, Number One." Grimes looked at his watch, the one that had been adjusted to keep Morrowvian time. "Mphm. Time Maya was here."

"And here she is," said Maggie. "Enter the Queen of Cambridge, singing and dancing. . . ."

Maya was not singing and dancing, but she looked well rested, alert, and as though she were looking forward to the outing. She was escorted by a half a dozen bow-women and a like number of spearmen, two of whom were carrying a large basket between them. Curiously, Grimes looked into the basket. There were bowls of the raw fish that he had enjoyed the previous day, other bowls of what looked like dried meat. He looked away hastily. All that he had been able to manage for breakfast was a large cup of black coffee.

Maya looked with interest at the pinnace. "How does this thing fly?" she asked. "I don't see any wings or gasbag. . . ."

"Inertial drive," Grimes told her briefly. "No, I'm sorry, but I can't explain it at this hour of the morning." He turned to Saul. "All right, Number One. I'm getting the show on the road. I leave *Seeker* in your capable hands. Don't do anything you couldn't do riding a bicycle."

"What *is* a bicycle?" asked Maya.

"Remind me to bring you one some time. . . ." He visualized the tall, lush, naked woman astride such a machine and felt more than a little happier.

Pitcher and Billard clambered into the pinnace. They stood in the open doorway and took the hamper of Maya's provisions as the two Morrowvian spearmen handed it up to them. Then, Maggie, disdaining the offer of a helping hand from Grimes, mounted the short ladder into the doorway. Grimes, however, was courteously able to assist Maya to board. He glared coldly at Saul when he noticed the sardonic look on the first lieutenant's face. Then he boarded himself.

Pitcher, with a chart made from Maggie's photographs, and young Mr. Billard occupied the forward compartment. Grimes sat with Maggie and Maya in the after cabin. As soon as the women were comfortable—although Maya was sitting on the edge of her seat like a young girl at her very first party—Grimes ordered, "Take her up."

"Take her up, sir," acknowledged Billard smartly. He was little more than a boy and inclined to take himself seriously, but he was able and conscientious. The noise of the restarted inertial drive was little more, at first, than a distant whisper. The pinnace lifted so gently that there was no sense of motion; even Grimes was surprised to see the sleek hull of *Seeker* sliding past and downward beyond the viewports. She ascended vertically, and then her passengers were able to look out and down at the two ships—*Southerly Buster*'s people were sleeping in; there were no signs of life around her—at the winding river, at the little towns spaced along its banks.

Maya ran from one side to the other of the small cabin. There was rather much of her in these confined quarters. "Oh, look!" she said, pointing. "There's *Cambridge!* Doesn't it look *small* from up here! And that town on the next bend is Kingston, and there's Richmond. . . . And there's the weekly cargo wherry, there, with the sail. . . ."

Grimes could not appreciate the distant view as it was obscured by Maya's breasts, but he did not complain.

"Sir," called Pitcher, "do you want us to steer a compass course, or shall we navigate from landmark to landmark? That way we shall not put on much distance."

"From landmark to landmark," said Grimes. "We may as well enjoy the scenery."

"You look as though you're doing that right now," commented Maggie.

"Would you mind getting back to your seat, Maya?" asked Grimes. "We shall be accelerating soon, and you may lose your balance. . . ."

"Make sure you don't lose yours . . ." Maggie murmured.

The irregular beat of the inertial drive was louder now, and its vibration noticeable. The pinnace turned in a wide arc, and then the landing site was astern of them, and the two, tall ships were dwindling to the size of toys. Ahead of them, and a little to starboard, was a snowcapped mountain, Ben Nevis. Below them was a wide prairie over which surged a great herd of duncolored beasts. "Bison," said Maya, adding that these animals constituted the main meat supply of her people. She offered strips of dried flesh from her basket to Grimes and Maggie, much as a Terran woman would offer chocolates. Grimes took one and chewed it dubiously. It wasn't bad, but it would not worry him much if he never tasted any more of it.

He took a pair of binoculars from their rack and stared down at the so-called bison. From almost directly above them he could not get much of an idea of their general appearance—but he knew that the

Terran animals of that name had never run to six legs, whereas these brutes did.

The gleaming peak of Ben Nevis hung in their starboard viewports for long seconds, then dropped slowly astern. The pinnace, now, was following the course of another river, the Mersey, and Maya was pointing out the towns along its meandering length. "Yes, that must be Lancaster. . . . I visited there two years ago, and I remember that thickly wooded hill just by it. . . . Most of the people living along the Mersey banks are Cordwainers. . . ."

"Cordwainers?" asked Grimes, thinking that she must be referring to some odd trade.

"It is their name, just as Smith is the name of most of us along the Thames. . . ."

"And what names, how many names, do you have on this world?" asked Maggie.

"There's Smith, of course. And Wells. And Morrow. And Cordwainer. That's all."

"Probably only four male survivors when *Lode Cougar* got here," said Grimes. "And polygamous marriages. . . ."

"Chester," announced Maya, pointing to another town. "Brighton, and the shipbuilding yards. . . . That schooner looks almost finished . . . Manchester, *I think*. . . . Oh, this is the way to travel! It took me weeks, many weeks, when I did it by foot and by wherry!"

"And why do you travel?" asked Maggie.

"Why do *you* travel?" the other woman countered. "To . . . to see new things, new people."

"And what new things have you seen?"

"Oh, the workshops at Manchester. You must have noticed the smoke as we flew over them. They smelt metal there, after they've dug the ore from the ground. They say that for years and years, before the process was discovered, we had to use scraps of metal from the ship to tip our spears and arrows."

"And so your weapons are made from this iron—I suppose it's iron—from Manchester?" asked Maggie.

"Yes."

"And what do you buy it with? What do you barter for it?"

"The salmon are caught only in the Thames. Their pickled flesh is a great delicacy."

"And tell me," Maggie went on, "don't some of you Smiths and Morrows and Wellses and Cordwainers get the idea, sometimes, that there are other ways of getting goods besides barter?"

"There are on other ways, Commander Maggie."

"On some worlds there are. Just suppose, Maya . . . just suppose that it's been a bad year for salmon. Just suppose that you need a stock of new weapons and have nothing to give in exchange for them. Just suppose that you lead a party of spearmen and archers to, say, Oxford, to take the people by surprise and to take their bows and spears by force. . . ."

"Are you mad?" demanded Maya. "That would be impossible. It is not . . . human to intrude where one is not wanted. As for . . . *fighting* . . . that is not human either. Oh, we fight the wolves, but only to protect ourselves from them. We fight the eagles when we have to. But to fight each other . . . unthinkable!''

"But you must fight sometimes," said Maggie.

"Yes. But we are ashamed of it afterward. Our young men, perhaps, over a woman. Sometimes two women will quarrel, and use their claws. Oh, we have all read The History. We know that human beings have fought each other, and with weapons that would make our spears and bows look like toys. But we *could* not.'' There was a long silence, broken when she asked timidly, "And can you?''

"I'm afraid we can," Grimes told her. "And I'm afraid that we do. Your world has no soldiers or policemen, but yours is an exceptional world. . . .''

"And are *you* a soldier, Commander Grimes?''

"Don't insult me, Maya. I'm a spaceman, although I am an officer in a fighting service. I suppose that you could call me a policeman of sorts. . . .''

"The policeman's lot is not a happy one . . .'' quoted Maggie solemnly.

"Mphm. Nobody press-ganged me into the Survey Service.''

Then they were approaching the coast, the mouth of the river and the port town of Liverpool. North they swept, running low over the glittering sea, deviating from their course to pass close to a large schooner, deviating again to make rings around a huge, unwieldy balloon, hovering over a fleet of small fishing craft whose crews were hauling in nets alive with a silvery catch, whose men stared upward in wonder at the alien flying machine.

Pitcher called back from the pilot's cabin, "We're

setting course for the mouth of the Yarra, sir—if you're agreeable.''

''I'm agreeable, Mr. Pitcher. You can put her on automatic and we'll have lunch.''

Maya enjoyed the chicken sandwiches that had been packed for them, and Pitcher and Billard waxed enthusiastic over the spiced fish that she handed around.

13

It was an uneventful flight northward over the ocean. They sighted no traffic save for a large schooner beating laboriously to windward; the Morrowvians, Grimes learned from Maya, were not a sea-minded people, taking to the water only from necessity and never for recreation.

As the pinnace drove steadily onward Maya, with occasional encouragement from Grimes and Maggie, talked. Once she got going she reminded Grimes of a Siamese cat he had once known, a beast even more talkative than the generality of its breed. So she talked, and Grimes and Maggie and Pitcher and Billard listened, and every so often Maggie would have to put a fresh spool in her recorder.

This Morrowvia was an odd sort of a planet—odd insofar as the population was concerned. The people were neither unintelligent nor illiterate, but they had fallen surprisingly far from the technological levels of the founders of the colony—and, even more surprisingly, the fall had been arrested at a stage well above primitive savagery. On so many worlds similarly settled the regression to Man's primitive beginnings had been horridly complete.

So there was Morrowvia, with a scattered population of ten million, give or take a few hundreds of thousands, all of them living in small towns, and all these towns with good old Terran names. There was no agriculture, save for the cultivation of herbs used medicinally and for the flavoring of food. Meat was obtained by hunting, although halfhearted attempts had been made at the domestication of the so-called bison and a few of the local flying creatures, more reptilian than anything else, the flesh and the eggs of which were palatable. The reason why more had not been done along these lines was that hunting was a way of life.

There was some industry—the mining and smelting of metals, the manufacture of weapons and such few tools as were required, shipbuilding. Should more ever be required, said Maya, the library at Ballarat would furnish full instructions for doing everything, for making anything at all.

Government? There was, said the Morrowvian woman, government of a sort. Each town was autonomous, however, and each was ruled—although "ruled" was hardly the correct word—by an elected queen. No, there were no kings. (Maya had read The History and knew what kings were.) It was only natural that women, who were in charge of their own homes, should elect a woman to be in overall charge of an assemblage of homes. It was only natural that the men should be occupied with male pursuits such as hunting and fishing—although women, the younger ones especially, enjoyed the hunt as much as the men did. And it was only natural that men should employ the spear as their main weapon, while women favored the bow.

No, there were no women engaged in heavy industry, although they did work at such trades as the manufacture of cordage and what little cloth was used. And women tended the herb gardens.

Maya confirmed that there were only four families—although "tribes" would be the better word—on Morrowvia. There were Smiths, Cordwainers, Morrows and Wellses. There was intermarriage between the tribes, and in such cases the husband took his wife's surname, which was passed on, also, to the children of such unions. It was not quite a matriarchal society, but it was not far from it.

Grimes steered the conversation on to the subject of communications. There had been radio—but many generations ago. It had never been required—"After all," said Maya reasonably enough, "if I die and my people elect a new queen it is of no real concern to anybody except themselves. There is no need for the entire planet to be informed within seconds of the event."—and transmitters and receivers had been allowed to fall into desuetude. There was a loosely organized system of postmen—men and women qualified by powers of endurance and fleetness of foot—but these carried only letters and very light articles of merchandise. Heavier articles were transported in the slow wherries, up and down the rivers—which meant that a consignment of goods would often have to be shipped along the two long sides of a triangle rather than over the short, overland side.

There was a more or less—rather less than more—regular service by schooner between the island continents. The seamen, Grimes gathered, were a race apart, males and females too incompetent to get by ashore—or, if not incompetent, too antisocial. Seafaring was a profession utterly devoid of either glamor or standing. Grimes was rather shocked when he heard this. He regarded himself as being in a direct line of descent from the seamen and explorers of Earth's past, and was of the opinion that ships, ships of any kind, were the finest flower of human civilization.

The airmen—the balloonists—were much more highly thought of, though the service they provided was even more unreliable than that rendered by the sailors. Some of the airmen, Maya said, were wanting to fit their clumsy, unmaneuverable craft with engines—but Morrow (he must have been quite a man, this Morrow, thought Grimes) had warned his people, shortly before his death, of the overuse of machinery.

He had said (Maya quoted), "I am leaving you a good world. The land, the air and the sea are clean. Your own wastes go back into the soil and render it more fertile. The wastes of the machines will pollute everything—the sky, the sea and the very ground you walk upon. Beware of the machine. It pretends to be a good servant—but the wages that it exacts are far too high."

"A machine brought you—your ancestors—here," pointed out Grimes.

"If that machine had worked properly we should

not be here," said Maya. She smiled. "The breaking down of the machine was our good luck."

"Mphm." But this was a *good* world. It could be improved—and what planet could not? But would the reintroduction of machinery improve it? The reintroduction not only of machinery but of the servants of the machine, that peculiar breed of men who have sold their souls to false gods of steam and steel, of metal and burning oil, who tend, more and more, to degrade humanity to the status of slaves, to elevate the mindless automata to the status of masters.

Even so . . . what was that quotation he had used in a recent conversation with Maggie? "Transportation is civilization."

More efficient transportation, communications in general, would improve Morrowvia. He said as much. He argued, "Suppose there's some sort of natural catastrophe . . . a hurricane, say, or a fire, or a flood. . . . If you had radio again, or efficient aircraft, the survivors could call for help, almost at once, and the help would not be long in reaching them."

"But why?" Maya asked. "But why? Why should *they* call for help, and why should *we* answer? Or why should *we* call for help, and why should *they* answer? We—how shall I put it? We go our ways, all of us, with neither help or hindrance, from anybody. We . . . cope. If disaster strikes, it is *our* disaster. We should not wish any interference from outsiders."

"A passion for privacy," remarked Maggie, "carried to extremes."

"Privacy is our way of life," Maya told her. "It is a good way of life."

Grimes had been wondering how soon it would be before the pair of them clashed; now the clash had come. They glared at each other, the two handsome women, one naked, the other in her too-skimpy uniform, somehow alike—and yet very unlike each other. Claws were being unsheathed.

And then young Billard called out from the forward compartment. "Land on the radar, sir! Looks like the coastline, at four hundred kilometers!"

Rather thankfully Grimes got up and went into the pilot's cabin. He looked into the screen of the radarscope, then studied the chart that had been made from the original survey data and from Maggie's photographs of that quite accurate wall map in Maya's "palace." Yes, that looked like Port Phillip Bay, with the mighty Yarra flowing into it from the north. He thought, *North Australia*, here we come! Then, with an affection of the Terran Australian accent, *Norstrylia, here we come!*

That corruption of words rang a faint but disturbing bell in his mind—but he had, as and from now, more important things to think about.

He said to the navigator, "A very nice landfall, Mr. Pitcher," and to Billard, "Better put her back on manual. And keep her as she's going."

Maya was by his side, looking with pleased wonderment at the glowing picture in the radar screen. Grimes thought, *I wish she wouldn't rub up against me so much. Not in front of Pitcher and Billard, anyhow. And not in front of Maggie, especially.*

14

It was summer in the northern hemisphere, and when the pinnace arrived over Melbourne, having followed the winding course of the Yarra to the foothills of the Dandenongs, there were still half a dozen hours of daylight left. The town, as were all the towns, was a small one; Grimes estimated that its population would run to about four thousand people. As they made the approach he studied it through powerful binoculars. It was neatly laid out, and the houses seemed to be of wooden construction, with thatched roofs. Beyond the town, on a conveniently sited patch of level, tree-free ground, towered the unmistakable metal steeple of a starship. There was only one ship that it could be.

Suddenly the pinnace's transceiver came to life. *"Schnauzer* calling strange aircraft. *Schnauzer* calling strange aircraft. Do you read me?"

"I read you," replied Grimes laconically.

"Identify yourself, please."

"Schnauzer, this is Number One Pinnace of FSS *Seeker.* Over."

There was a silence. Then, "You may land by me, Number One Pinnace."

Grimes looked at Pitcher and Billard. They looked back at him. He raised an eyebrow sardonically. Pitcher said, "Uncommonly decent of him, sir, to give *us* permission to land. . . ."

"Mphm. I suppose he was here first—although I don't think that planting a shipping company's flag makes a territorial claim legally valid."

"They could rename this world Pomerania . . ." suggested Pitcher.

"Or Alsatia . . ." contributed Billard.

"Or New Pekin . . ." continued Pitcher. "Or some other son-of-a-bitching name. . . ."

"Or Dogpatch," said Grimes, with an air of finality. And then, into the microphone, an edge of sarcasm to his voice. "Thank you, *Schnauzer*. I am coming in."

Acting on his captain's instructions Billard brought the pinnace low over the town. People stared up at them—some in the by now familiar state of nudity, some clothed. Those who were dressed were wearing uniform, obviously personnel from the Dog Star ship. The small craft almost grazed the peaked, thatched roofs, then settled down gently fifty meters to the west of *Schnauzer*, on the side from which her boarding ramp was extended.

"Well," remarked Maggie, "we're here. I don't notice any red carpet out for us. What do we do now?"

"We disembark," Grimes told her. "There'll be no need to leave anybody aboard; the officers of major shipping companies are usually quite law-abiding people." *Ususaily*, he thought, *but not al-*

ways. He remembered suddenly the almost piratical exploits of one Captain Craven, the master of *Delta Orionis,* to which he, Grimes, had been an accessory.

"What about Drongo Kane?" asked Maggie.

"You can hardly call *him* a major shipping company," said Grimes.

Three men were walking slowly down the merchant ship's ramp. In the lead was a bareheaded, yellow-haired giant, heavily muscled. Following him was a tall and slender, too slender, young man. Finally—last ashore and first to board—was a portly gentleman, clothed in dignity and respectability as well as in master's uniform. All of them wore sidearms. Grimes frowned. As a naval officer he did not like to see merchant officers going about armed to the teeth—but he knew that the Dog Star Line held quite strong views on the desirability of the ability of its ships and its personnel to defend themselves.

The door of the pinnace opened and the short ladder extended itself to the grassy ground. Grimes buckled on his belt with the holstered pistol, put on his cap and, ignoring the steps, jumped out of the small craft. He turned to assist Maggie but she ignored his hand, jumped also. Maya followed her, leaping down with feline grace. Pitcher was next, then Billard, who spoiled the effect by tripping and sprawling untidily.

Schnauzer's master had taken leading place now, and was advancing slowly, with his two officers a couple of paces to the rear. Unlike them he was not wearing the comfortable, utilitarian gray shorts, shirt and stockings but a white uniform, with tunic and long trousers—but portly men look their best in clothing that conceals most of the body.

He acknowledged Grimes's salute stiffly, while his rather protuberant brown eyes flickered over the young man's insignia of rank. He said, in a rather reedy voice, "Good afternoon, Commander." Then, "You are the commanding officer of *Seeker?*"

"Yes, Captain. Lieutenant Commander Grimes. And you, sir, are Captain Roger Danzellan, and the two gentlemen with you are Mr. Oscar Eklund, chief officer, and Mr. Francis Delamere, second officer."

"How right you are, Commander. I realize that there is no need for me to introduce myself and my people. But as a mere merchant captain I do not have the resources of an Intelligence Service to draw upon. . . ."

Grimes took the hint and introduced Maggie, Maya, Pitcher and Billard.

"And now, Commander," asked Danzellan, "what can I do for you?"

"If you would, sir, you can tell me what you are doing here."

"Trade, Commander, trade. This is a competitive galaxy, although you ladies and gentlemen in the Survey Service may not find it so. My employers are not in business for the state of their health. . . ."

"Aren't they?" inquired Maggie. "I would have thought that the state of their *financial* health was their main concern."

"A point well taken, Commander Lazenby. Anyhow, the Dog Star Line is always ready and willing to expand its sphere of operations. When a Dog Star ship, *Corgi*–but I imagine that you know all about *that*–stumbled upon this world, quite by chance, the reports made by her master, myself were read with great interest by the Board of Directors. It was realized that we, as it were, have one foot well inside the door. It was decided to strike the iron while it is hot. Do you read me, Commander Grimes?''

"Loud and clear, Captain Danzellan. But tell me, what sort of trade do you hope to establish with the people of Morrowvia?''

"There are manufactured goods from a score of planets on our established routes for which there will be a demand here. For example, I have in my hold a large consignment of solar-powered refrigerators, and one of solar cookers. On the occasion of my first visit here a refrigerator was left with the, er, Queen of Melbourne. I was pleased to discover on my return that it is still working well, and even more pleased to learn that other, er, queens have seen it, and that still others have heard about it. . . .''

"You will remember, Commander Grimes,'' said Maya, "that I told you about the cold box.''

"So even this lady, from Cambridge, many miles from here, has heard about it.''

"Mphm. But how are the people going to pay the freight on these quite unnecessary luxuries—and for the luxuries themselves?''

"Unnecessary luxuries, Commander? I put it to you—would *you* be prepared to sip your pre-prandial pink gin without an ice cube to make it more potable? Do *you* enjoy lukewarm beer?''

"Frankly, no, Captain. But—the question of payment. . . ."

"These are sordid details, Commander. But I have no doubt that something will be worked out."

"No doubt at all," commented Maggie Lazenby. "When people want something badly enough they find some way of paying for it."

"In a nutshell, Commander Lazenby. In a nutshell." Danzellan beamed upon her benignly. Then, "I am sorry that I cannot ask you aboard my ship, but we are rather cramped for space. In a merchant vessel carrying capacity for money-earning cargo is of greater importance than luxurious accommodation for personnel."

"I understand," said Grimes. Such merchant vessels as he had been aboard housed their officers in far greater comfort than did the Survey Service. He went on, "Maya, here, wishes to pay her respects to her sister queen. We will accompany her."

"I'll show you the way, Commander," volunteered Mr. Delamere eagerly.

Danzellan frowned at his second officer and the young man wilted visibly. Then the captain relented. "All right," he said. "You may take the party from *Seeker* to Queen Lilian's palace." He added sternly, "See that they don't get lost."

15

Delamere led the way from the landing site to the town, walking fast. He did not pause when he took the party past a survey team from *Schnauzer*, busily engaged with tapes, rods and theodolite, working under the direction of a young woman with third officer's braid on her shoulderboards. He acknowledged her wave absently. Watching the surveyors was a large group of children, with a smaller number of adults. These people, Grimes saw, were very similar to those whom he had encountered at *Seeker's* landing place—well formed, beautiful rather than merely handsome. He was interested to note, however, that here the rudimentary nipples below the true breasts were the exception rather than the rule, whereas among Maya's people almost every woman—as she herself—was so furnished.

The dirt roads between the houses were level and tidy. The wooden buildings were well spaced and these, unlike those in Cambridge, had glazed windows—but, probably, the winters on this continent would be relatively severe. There was an amplitude of trees and flowering shrubs in every open space.

Lilian's palace was larger than the other houses. It had, like Maya's a tall staff standing outside its main entrance, a pole surmounted by a star fabricated from glittering metal rods. Also, in the full light of the westering sun, there stood just outside the door a metallic box, mounted on small wheels. Grimes had seen such contraptions before; this was the famous sun-powered refrigerator.

A tall woman came out to meet them. Her skin was creamy; the hair of her head and body was a glowing orange color. She said to Maya, "Welcome, sister. My house is yours."

"Thank you, sister," replied Maya. Then, "We have corresponded, but I did not think that we should ever meet."

"You are . . . ?"

"Maya, from Cambridge, Lilian."

"I know of you, Maya. Now I have the pleasure of knowing you."

"Lilian . . ." said Delamere.

"Yes, Francis?"

"How is Tabitha?"

"She is well, Francis."

"Can I see her, Lilian?"

"It will be well if you do not, Francis. Unless you are willing to abide by our customs."

The young man looked desperately unhappy. His long nose quivered like that of a timid rabbit. He said, "But you know . . ."

"What do I know, Francis? Only what I am told. Only what I see with my own eyes." (*And those green eyes*, thought Grimes, *will see plenty.*)

"Lilian," Maya said, "I have brought friends with me."

"So I see." The woman was regarding the people from *Seeker* with a certain lack of enthusiasm. Her attitude seemed to be, *If you've seen one stranger from beyond the stars, you've seen them all.*

"Lilian, this is Commander Grimes, captain of the ship called *Seeker*. The lady is Commander Maggie Lazenby. The gentlemen are Lieutenant Pitcher and Ensign Billard."

Grimes saluted. Lilian Morrow inclined her head gravely, then said, "Be pleased to enter."

They followed her into the palace. Inside it was very like Maya's official residence, the big wall map being the most prominent decoration on a wall of the room into which she led them. She saw them seated, then excused herself and went back outside. While she was gone Grimes asked Delamere, "Who is Tabitha, Mr. Delamere?"

The second mate flushed angrily and snapped, "None of your business, Commander." Then, obviously regretting his display of temper, he muttered sulkily, "She's Lilian's daughter. I . . . I met her when I was here before, in *Corgi*. Now her mother won't let me see her again unless . . ."

"Unless what?" prompted Maggie. "Unless what, Francis?"

That's right, thought Grimes. *Turn on the womanly charm and sympathy.*

Delamere was about to answer when Lilian returned. She was carrying a tray on which was a rather lopsided jug of iced water, a dish of some greenish

looking flesh cut into cubes, glass drinking bowls.
She filled a bowl for each of them from the jug.

The water was refreshing, the meat tasted how
Grimes imagined that the flesh of a snake would
taste. He supposed—he hope—that it was non-
poisonous. Maya seemed to be enjoying it.

"And now, Commander Grimes," asked Lilian,
after they had all sipped and nibbled, "what do you
here?"

"I represent the Federation, Lilian. . . ."

"Just as Captain Danzellan represents the Dog
Star Line. Captain Danzellan hopes to make
money—and Morrow warned us about *that*—for his
employers and himself. And what do *you* hope to
make for yourself and your employers?"

"We are here to help you, Lilian."

"Do we need any help, Commander Grimes?"

"The Survey Service, Lilian, is like a police
force. You know what a police force is. You have
read The History. We protect people from those
who would exploit them, rob them, even."

"Have we asked for protection?"

"You may do so."

"But we have not done so."

"Yet."

"Lilian knows that she has nothing to fear from
us," said Delamere, more than a little smugly.

"Indeed, Francis?" The look that she gave him
drove him back into sullen silence. Then she addressed Grimes again. "Commander Grimes, the relationship established between ourselves and Captain
Danzellan is, on the whole, a friendly one. Captain

Danzellan, in exchange for certain concessions, will bring us goods that we cannot make for ourselves. Before anything is decided, however, it will be necessary to convene a Council of Queens. I, of course, speak only for Melbourne—but Morrow foresaw that a time would come when matters affecting the entire continent, the entire world, even, would have to be discussed. Word has gone to my sisters of Ballarat, Alice, Darwin, Sydney, Perth, Brisbane—but there is no need for me to recite to you the names of all the towns of North Australia—that decisions affecting us all must soon be made. It is fortunate that our sister of Cambridge is with us; she will be able to report to her own people on what we are doing.''

''These concessions . . .'' began Grimes.

''They are none of *your* business, Commander.''

Grimes looked appealingly at Maggie. She was supposed to know what made people tick. She was supposed to know which button to push to get which results. She looked back at him blandly.

Damn the woman! thought Grimes. *Damn* all *women.* He floundered on, ''But perhaps I should be able to advise you. . . .''

''We do not need your advice, Commander.''

''Mphm.'' Grimes fished his battered pipe from his pocket, filled it, lit it.

''Please!'' said Lilian sharply, ''do not smoke that filthy thing in here!''

''So your great ancestor warned you about smoking. . . .''

''He did so. He warned us about all the vices and

unpleasant habits of the men who, eventually, would make contact with us.''

''Oh, well,'' muttered Grimes at last. Then, ''I suppose that there is no objection to our visiting Ballarat, to look at your library, your records. . . .''

''That is a matter for the Queen of Ballarat.''

And there isn't any radio, thought Grimes, *and there aren't any telephones, and I'm damned if I'll ask Her Majesty here to send a messenger.* He said, ''Thank you for your hospitality, Lilian. And now, if you will excuse us, we'll get back to our pinnace and set up camp for the night.''

She said, ''You are excused. And you have my permission to sleep on the outskirts of the town.''

''Shall we set up a tent for you, Maya? Grimes asked.

''Thank you, no. Lilian and I have so much to talk about.''

''Can I see Tabitha?'' pleaded Delamere.

''No, Francis. You may not.''

Schnauzer's second officer got reluctantly to his feet. He mumbled, ''Are you ready, Commander? I'm getting back to my ship.''

He led the way out of the palace and back to the landing site, although his services as a guide were hardly necessary. *Schnauzer*, dwarfing the trees that grew around the grassy field, stuck up like a sore thumb.

Back at the pinnace Grimes, Pitcher and Billard unloaded their camping gear, with Maggie watching and, at times, criticizing. The little air compresser swiftly inflated the four small sleeping tents, the larger one that would combine the functions of mess-room and galley. Then Billard went to the nearby stream for two buckets of water. A sterilizing tablet was dropped into each one, more as a matter of routine than anything else. If the broad spectrum antibiotic shots administered aboard *Seeker* had not been effective it would have been obvious by now. The battery-powered cooker was set up, and in a short time a pot of savory stew, prepared from de-hydrated ingredients, was simmering and water was boiling for coffee.

The four of them sat around the collapsible table waiting until the meal was ready.

Grimes said, "What do you make of it, Maggie?"

"Make of what?" she countered.

"The whole setup."

She replied thoughtfully. "There's something *odd* about this world. In the case of Sparta there were all sorts of historical analogies to draw upon—here, there aren't. And how shall I put it? Like this, perhaps. The Morrowvians rather resent the viola-tion of their privacy, but realize that there's nothing much that they can do about it. They certainly aren't mechanically minded, and distrust of the machine has been bred into them—but they do appreciate that the machine can contribute greatly to their comfort. I imagine that Danzellan's 'cold boxes' will be *very* popular. . . . As for their attitude toward ourselves—there's distrust again, but I think that they are prepared to like us as individuals. Maya, for example, has taken quite a shine to you. I've been expecting to see you raped at any tick of the clock. . . ."

"Mphm."

"You could do worse, I suppose—though whether or not she could is another matter. . . ."

"Ha, ha," chuckled Pitcher politely.

"Hah. Hah," growled Grimes, inhibiting any further mirth on the part of his subordinates.

"Anyhow, as far as behavior goes they do tend to deviate widely from the norm. The *human* norm, that is. . . ."

"What do you mean?" asked Grimes.

"I rather wish that I knew, myself," she told him.

16

Grimes had Pitcher work out the local time of sunrise, then saw to it that everybody had his watch alarm set accordingly. Before retiring he called Saul aboard *Seeker*—his wrist transceiver was hooked up to the much more powerful set in the pinnace—and listened to his first lieutenant's report of the day's activities. Mr. Saul had little to tell him. Maya's people had made considerable inroads into the ship's supply of ice cream. Sabrina's people had been coming and going around *Southerly Buster* all day, but neither Sabrina nor Captain Kane had put in an appearance. Saul seemed to be shocked by this circumstance. Grimes shrugged. Drongo's morals—or lack of them—were none of his concern.

Or were they?

Grimes then told Saul, in detail, of his own doings of the day, of his plans for the morrow. He signed off, undressed, wriggled into his sleeping bag. Seconds after he had switched off his portable light he was soundly asleep.

The shrilling of the alarm woke him just as the almost level rays of the rising sun were striking through the translucent walls of his tent. He got up, went outside into the fresh, cool morning, sniffed appreciatively the tangy scent of dew-wet grass. Somewhere something that probably was nothing at all like a bird was sounding a series of bell-like notes. There were as yet no signs of life around *Schnauzer*, although the first thin, blue drift of smoke from cooking fires was wreathing around the thatched rooftops of Melbourne.

Grimes walked down to the river to make his toilet. He was joined there by Pitcher and Billard. The water was too cold for the three men to linger long over their ablutions, although the heat of the sun was pleasant on their naked bodies. As they were walking back to the camp Maggie passed them on her way to her own morning swim. She told them that she had made coffee.

Soon the four of them were seated round the table in the mess tent to a breakfast of reconstituted scrambled egg and more coffee. Rather surprisingly they were joined there by Maya. The Morrowvian woman put out a dainty hand and scooped up a small sample of the mess on Grimes's plate, tasted it. She complained, "I don't like this."

"Frankly, neither do I," admitted Grimes, "but it's the best we can offer." He masticated and swallowed glumly. "And what can we do for you this morning?"

She said, "I am coming with you."

"Good. Do you know the Queen of Ballarat?"

"I know of her. And Lilian has given me a letter of introduction." With her free hand she tapped the small bag of woven straw that she was carrying.

"Then let's get cracking," said Grimes.

While Maggie, with Maya assisting rather ineffectually, washed the breakfast things Grimes, with Pitcher and Billard doing most of the work, struck and stowed the sleeping tents. Then the furniture and other gear from the mess tent was loaded aboard the pinnace, and finally the mess tent itself was deflated and folded and packed with the other gear.

From the pinnace Grimes called *Seeker*, told Saul that he was getting under way. While he was doing so Billard started the inertial drive, and within seconds the small craft was lifting vertically. As she drew level with *Schnauzer*'s control room Grimes could see figures standing behind the big viewports. He picked up his binoculars for a better look. Yes, there was the portly figure of Captain Danzellan, and with him was Eklund, his mate.

"Take her south for a start, sir?" asked Pitcher. "And then, once we're out of *Schnauzer*'s sight, we can bring her round on the course for Ballarat. . . ."

"No," decided Grimes. The same idea had occurred to him—but Lilian knew his destination, and she was at least on speaking terms with Danzellan and his officers. In any case—as compared with Drongo Kane—the Dog Star people were goodies, and if anything went badly wrong they would be in a position to offer immediate help. "No," he said again. "Head straight for Ballarat."

Ballarat was different from the other towns that they had seen. It was dominated by a towering structure, a great hulk of metal, pitted and weathered yet still geaming dully in the morning sunlight. It was like no ship that Grimes or his officers had ever seen—although they had seen pictures and models of such ships in the astronautical museum at the Academy. It was a typical gaussjammer of the days of the Second Expansion, a peg-top-shaped hull with its wide and uppermost, buttressed by flimsy looking fins. To land her here, not far from the magnetic equator, her captain must have been a spaceman of no mean order—or must have been actuated by desperation. It could well have been that his passengers and crew were so weakened by starvation that a safe landing, sliding down the vertical lines of force in the planet's solar regions, would have been safe for the ship only, not for her personnel. Only the very hardy can survive the rigors of an arctic climate.

Hard by the ship was a long, low building. As seen from the air it seemed to be mainly of wooden construction, although it was roofed with sheets of gray metal. No doubt there had been cannibalization; no doubt many nonessential bulkheads and the like were missing from the gaussjammer's internal structure.

Billard brought the pinnace in low over the town. There were people in the streets, mainly women and children. They looked upward and pointed. Some of them waved. And then, quite suddenly, a smoky fire was lit in a wide plaza to the east of the gaussjammer. It was a signal, obviously. The tall streamer of smoke rose vertically into the still air.

"That's where we land," said Grimes. "Take her down, please, Mr. Billard."

"Aye, aye, sir!"

Quietly, without any fuss or bother, they landed. Even before the door was open, even before the last mutterings of the inertial drive had faded into silence, they heard the drums, a rhythmic thud and rattle, an oddly militaristic sound.

"Mphm?" grunted Grimes dubiously. He turned to Maya. "Are you sure the natives are friendly?"

She did not catch the allusion. "Of course," she said stiffly. "*Everybody* on Morrowvia is friendly. A queen is received courteously by her sister queens wherever she may go."

"I'm not a queen," said Grimes. "I'm not a king, even. . . ."

"The way you carry on sometimes, aboard your ship, I'm inclined to doubt the validity of that last statement," remarked Maggie Lazenby.

"Open up, sir?" asked Billard.

"Mphm. Yes. But nobody is to go outside—except myself—until I give the word. And you'd better have the twenty millimeters ready for use, Mr. Pitcher."

He belted on his pistols—one projectile, one laser—then set his cap firmly on his head. Maya said, "I am coming with you."

Grimes said, "I'm not in the habit of hiding behind a woman's skirts."

"What skirts?" asked Maggie Lazenby. Then, "Don't be silly, John. Maya's obviously one of *them*. When they see her with you they'll know that you're friendly."

It made sense.

Grimes jumped down from the open door to the packed earth of the plaza, clapping each hand to a pistol butt as soon as he was on the ground. Maya followed him. They stood there, listening to the rhythmic *tap-tappity-tap* that was, with every second, louder and louder.

And then a women—a girl—appeared from around the end of the long, low building. She was naked save for polished high boots and a crimson sash, and was carrying a flag on a staff, a black flag with a stylized great cat, in gold, rampant over a compass rose. Behind her marched the drummers, also girls, and behind them a woman with a silver sash and with a silver crown set on her silvery hair. She was followed by six men, with spears, six female archers, and by six more men, each of whom carried what was obviously an automatic rifle of archaic design.

Abruptly the drums fell silent and the drummers divided their ranks to let the queen pass through. She advanced steadily, followed by her standard bearer. Her skin was black and gleaming, but there was no hint of negroid ancestry in her regular features. Apart from the absence of rudimentary nipples she was what Grimes was coming to consider a typical Morrowvian woman.

Grimes saluted.

The standard bearer dipped her flag.

The queen smiled sweetly and said, "I, Janine Morrow, welcome you to Ballarat—the landing place of *Lode Cougar* and of our forebears. I welcome you, spaceman, and I welcome you, sister."

"Thank you," said Grimes. (Should he call this definitely regal female "Your Majesty" or not?)

"Thank you, Janine," said Maya. "I am Maya, of Cambridge."

"Thank you, Janine," said Grimes. "I am John Grimes, of the Federation Survey Service ship *Seeker*."

17

Grimes called the others down from the pinnace and introductions were made. Then Janine led the way to her palace, which was the long, low building hard by the ancient spaceship. In a room like the other rooms in which they had been similarly entertained there was the ritual sharing of food and water, during which the Queen of Ballarat read the letter that Maya had brought. Grimes was about to get a glimpse of it during her perusal; the paper was coarse-textured and gray rather than white, and the words had been scrawled upon it with a blunt pencil.

Janine said, "Lilian is favored. Twice she has been visited by Captain Danzellan, and now Commander Grimes is calling on her."

"Now Commander Grimes is calling on *you*," Maya pointed out.

"And so he is." Janine smiled sweetly, her teeth very white and her lips very red in her dark brown face. "And so he is. But what brings you to Ballarat, Commander Grimes? Do you have gifts for me?"

"I shall have gifts for you—but I have nothing at the moment. You will appreciate that we cannot carry much in a small craft such as my pinnace."

"That is true," agreed Janine. "But every time that Captain Danzellan has wished to look for information in the museum or the library he has brought me something." She gestured toward one of the walls where a new-looking clock, with a brightly gleaming metal case, was hanging. "That is a *good* clock—far better than the old one with its dangling weights. This one does not have a spring even—just a power cell which Captain Danzellan tells me will be good for centuries."

"From the way that you greeted us," said Grimes, "I thought that you were pleased to see visitors from the home world of your ancestors."

"But I am, I am! Too, it pleases me to try to—what is the word?—to reconstruct the old rituals. I have studied The History, as have we all. Also, I have access to records which my sisters elsewhere have not. I received you as important visitors must be received on Earth. . . ."

"Mphm."

"I am sorry that I could not fire a salute, but we have no big guns. In any case, the supply of ammunition for our rifles is limited."

"You did very nicely," said Grimes.

"Bring on the marching girls . . ." muttered Maggie.

Grimes, surreptitiously, had eased his watch off his wrist. The instrument was almost new; he had purchased it from the commissary just prior to departure from Lindisfarne. He said, "Perhaps you will accept this, Janine. It is a personal timekeeper."

"Just what I've always wanted," she said, pleased.

"I take it, then," said Grimes, "that you are the custodian of the books, the records, the . . ."

"Of everything," she told him proudly. "Perhaps, while Maya and I have a gossip, you would care to be shown around?"

"We should," said Grimes.

Their guide was the young woman who had carried the banner. Her name was Lisa Morrow. She vouchsafed the information that it was usually she who conducted visiting queens from other towns through the palace, but that it was the first time that she had been responsible for a party of outworlders. She did not seem to be greatly impressed by the honor, or even to regard it as such.

The palace was more than a palace. It was a library, and it was a museum. They were taken first of all into the Earth Room, a huge chamber devoted to Earth as it had been when *Lode Cougar* had lifted from Port Woomera on her last voyage. This had been the overcrowded planet dominated, in its northern and southern hemispheres respectively, by the short-lived Russian and Australian Empires.

Lode Cougar, concluded Grimes, had carried a lot of junk—but even in the days of the Third Expansion a ticket out to the stars was very often a one-way ticket; it was even more so in the days of the First and Second Expansions. Those first colonists had been so reluctant to break every tie with their home world.

Here, in the Earth Room, were maps and photographs, reproductions of famous works of art, even files of newspapers and magazines. These latter had been chemically treated to make the paper impervious to mormal wear and tear, but now were practically unreadable—and Lisa Morrow took good care her charges did not, as they would have loved to have done, leaf through them. Grimes could make out the headlines on the front page of one of the papers, *The Australian*. *"Lode Tiger* missing, feared lost.'' No doubt the same paper had carried similar headlines regarding *Lode Cougar*. This had been long before the days of trained telepaths or the time-and-space-twisting Carlotti Communications System, but the established colonies had maintained a reasonably fast mail service with Earth. Grimes had read somewhere that it had taken less time for a letter to get from Port Southern, on Austral, to Sydney, in Australia, than it did to get through the post offices at either end. This state of affairs had persisted until the introduction of Carlotti radio transmission of all correspondence.

There were books, too—*real* books, properly bound, although with very thin, lightweight covers and paper. There were shelves of *How To* volumes. House building, boat building, aircraft building . . . mining, smelting, casting . . . navigation . . . surveying. . . . Useful, Grimes supposed, if you did not, as you were supposed to do, finish up at an established colony but, instead, made a forced landing on a hitherto undiscovered world.

There was fiction—but, in spite of their age, these books looked almost fresh from the printers. Grimes had suspected that the Morrowvians were oddly lacking in imagination. Anything factual—such as the famous History—they would read, or any book that would aid them to acquire necessary skills. But the products of the storyteller's art left them cold. This attitude was not uncommon, of course, but it seemed more pronounced here than elsewhere. What books had Danzellan given to Lilian on the occasion of his first visit? Grimes asked Lisa the question.

She told him, "One by a man called Blenkinshop on first aid. And one about the fisheries on a world called Atlantia. We are having copies made for the library."

"So you have a printing press?"

"Yes, Commander Grimes. It is used only when a book is almost worn out or when there is something new that has to be printed."

"Is it hand operated?"

"No. We have an engine, driven by steam. Shall I show it to you now, or would you rather see the *Lode Cougar* room?"

"The *Lode Cougar* room," Grimes told her.

This adjoined the Earth Room, but was not as large. It contained relics of the ship herself. There were cargo manifests, log books, crew and passenger lists. There was a large photograph of the *Cougar's* officers taken at Port Woomera, presumably shortly prior to lift-off. It was typical of this sort of portraiture, whatever the day and age. The captain, his senior officers on either side of him, was seated in the front row, his arms folded across his chest (as were the arms of the others) to show the braid on his sleeves. Standing behind the row of seated seniors were the juniors. Grimes stopped to read the legend below the photograph.

The captain's name was not, as he had expected

that it would be, Morrow. (But in an emergency, such as a forced landing on an unexplored world, anybody at all is liable to come to the fore.) The name of Morrow was not among those of the officers. A passenger, then? Examination of the ship's passenger list would supply the answer.

Lisa was pointing to a shelf of volumes. "And these," she was saying, "were Morrow's own books. . . ."

Grimes paused on his way to the display cases in which the ship's documents were housed. Books told one so much about their owner's makeup. His eye swept over the fiction titles. He realized, with pleased surprise, that he had read most of them, when he was a cadet at the Academy. Early Twentieth Century—and even late Nineteenth Century— science fiction aboard a starship! But it was no more absurd than to find the same science fiction required reading for future officers of a navy whose ships, even though they had yet to penetrate to The Hub, fared out to The Rim. *The Planet Buyer* . . . that had been good, as he remembered it. *The Island Of* . . .

His wrist transceiver was buzzing. He raised the instrument to his mouth. "Captain!" Saul's voice was urgent. "Captain, I would have called you before, but we've been having transmitter trouble. Drongo Kane left in his pinnace at first light this morning, heading north. He's got Sabrina with him and three of his own people, all armed."

"You heard that?" Grimes demanded of his officers.

They nodded.

"Thank you for your attention," Grimes said to Lisa, "but we must get back to our pinnace."

"Is Drongo Kane a friend of yours, that you are so eager to greet him?" she asked innocently, and looked bewildered when Grimes replied, "That'd be the sunny Friday!"

18

Grimes paused briefly in the room where Janine was still gossiping with Maya. As he entered he heard Maya ask, "And how do *you* deal with the problem of the uncontrollable adolescent?"

He said, "Excuse me, ladies. I've just received word that Drongo Kane is on his way here. . . ."

"Drongo Kane?" asked Janine, arching her silver brows.

"The captain of a ship called the *Southerly Buster*," Maya told her. "A *most* generous man."

"Goodie goodie," exclaimed her sister queen. She looked rather pointedly at Danzellan's gleaming clock on the wall, then at Grimes's watch that was strapped around her slim, brown wrist.

"Perhaps he'll give you an egg timer . . ." suggested Maggie Lazenby.

"What is that?" asked Janine.

"It's not important," said Grimes impatiently. "Excuse us, please."

He led the way out of the palace, to where his pinnace was grounded in the middle of the plaza, looking like a huge, stranded silver fish. He looked up at the clear sky. Yes—there, far to the southward, was a tiny speck, a dark dot against the blueness that expanded as he watched. Then he was aware that the two queens had followed him outside.

"Is that Drongo Kane?' asked Janine.

"I think it is," he replied.

"Then I must prepare a proper reception," she said and walked rapidly back to her palace. Maya stayed with Grimes.

She said, "Janine prides herself on doing things properly."

"If she were doing things properly," Grimes told her, "she would have a battery of ground to air missiles standing by."

"You must be joking!" she exclaimed, shocked.

"Have our own armament in readiness, sir?" asked the navigator.

"Mphm. I *was* joking, Mr. Pitcher. But it will do no harm to have the twenty millimeters cocked and ready."

Two women were building another fire in the brazier that had served Grimes for a beacon. One of them produced a large box of oversized matches from the pouch that she wore slung from her shoulder, lit the kindling. Almost immediately the column of gray smoke was climbing skyward.

Kane's pinnace was audible now as well as visible, the irregular beat of its inertial drive competing with the more rhythmic efforts of Janine's drummers, warming up behind the palace. It was coming in fast, and it seemed that it would overshoot the plaza. But Kane—presumably it was he at the controls—brought the craft to a spectacular, shuddering halt when it was almost directly over *Seeker*'s pinnace, applying maximum reverse thrust. That would not, thought Grimes disapprovingly, do his engines any good—but he, himself, had often been guilty of similar showmanship.

Oddly enough no crowd had gathered—but no crowd had gathered to greet Grimes. There were only a few deliberately uninterested bystanders, and they were mainly children. On no other world had Grimes seen such a fanatical respect for privacy.

Drongo Kane was dropping down now—not fast, yet not with extreme caution. His vertical thrust made odd patterns in the dust as the pinnace descended, not unlike those made in an accumulation of iron filings by a magnetic field. When there was little more than the thickness of a coat of paint between his landing gear and the ground he checked his descent, then cut his drive.

The door in the side of the pinnace opened. Drongo Kane stood in the opening. He was rigged up in a uniform that was like the full dress of the Survey Service—with improvements. An elaborate gold cockade ornamented his cocked hat, and his sword belt was golden, as was the scabbard. A score of decorations blazed over the left breast of his frock coat. Grimes thought he recognized the Iron Cross of Waldegren, the Golden Wings of the Hallichek Hegemony. Anybody who was highly regarded by those two governments would be *persona non grata* in decent society.

Kane jumped lightly to the ground, seemingly

unhampered by his finery. He extended a hand to help Sabrina from the pinnace. Jewels glittered on her smooth, golden skin, and a coronet ablaze with emeralds was set on her head. She was inclined to teeter a little in her unaccustomed, high-heeled sandals.

"Cor stone me Aunt Fanny up a gum tree!" whispered Maggie.

"Captain Kane is *generous*," murmured Maya.

"Mphm," grunted Grimes.

Inside the pinnace two of Kane's officers—and they were dressed only in their drab working uniforms—were setting up some sort of machine, an affair of polished brass, just within the doorway. Grimes stared at it in amazement and horror.

"Captain Kane," he shouted, "I forbid you to terrorize these people!'

Kane grinned cheerfully. "Keep your hair on, Commander! Nobody's goin' to terrorize anybody. Don't you recognize a salutin' cannon when you see one? Sabrina, here, has told me that this Queen Janine is a stickler for etiquette. . . ." Then his eyes widened as, to the rattle of drums, the procession emerged from around the corner of the palace. He licked his lips as he stared at the high-stepping girl with the *Lode Cougar* flag—that sash and those boots—especially the boots—did something for her. He muttered to himself, "And you can say *that* again!"

With a last ruffle of drums Janine and her entourage came to a halt. Kane drew himself to attention and saluted grandly. "Fire one!" snapped somebody inside the pinnace. The brass cannon boomed, making a noise disproportionate to its size. "Fire two!" Again there was the gout of orange flame, the billowing of dirty white smoke. "Fire three!"

At first it looked as though the spearmen, archers and riflemen would either turn and run—or loose their weapons off against the spacemen—but Janine snapped a sharp order and, drawing herself up proudly, stood her ground.

"Fire four!" *Boom!*

"Fire five!"

Janine was enjoying the show. So was Kane. Sabrina, at his side, winced every time the gun was fired, but tried to look as though this sort of thing was an everyday occurrence. Maya whispered urgently to Grimes, "This *noise* . . . can't you make him stop it?"

"Fire nine!" *Boom!*

"Fire ten!"

Janines bodyguard had recovered their composure now and were standing at stiff attention, and there was a certain envy evident in the expressions on the faces of the drummer girls—but the standard bearer spoiled the effect when the drifting fumes of the burning black powder sent her into a fit of sneezing.

"Fire sixteen!" *Boom!*

Surely not, thought Grimes dazedly. *Surely not. A twenty-one gun salute for somebody who, even though she is called a queen, is no more than the major of a small town. . . .*

"Fire twenty!" *Boom!*

"Fire twenty-one!" *Boom!*

"A lesson," remarked Maggie, "on how to win friends and influence people. . . ."

"He certainly influenced me!" said Grimes.

Kane, accompanied by Sabrina, marched to where Janine was standing. He saluted again. Janine nodded to him regally. The standard bearer, recovered from her sneezing fit, dipped her flag toward him. The spearmen and riflemen presented arms. Grimes watched all this a little enviously. He was sorry that Maya had not briefed him regarding Janine's love of ceremonial, as obviously Sabrina had briefed Kane. But it could be that Kane knew Sabrina far better than he, Grimes, knew Maya. There are more things to do in a shared bed than talking—but talking in bed is quite a common practice. . . .

"Shall I fire a burst from the twenty millimeters," asked Pitcher wistfully, "just to show that we can make a noise too?"

"No," Grimes said sternly.

"Sir," called Billard, "here comes another pinnace!"

Danzellan's arrival on the scene was anticlimactic. When he came in to a landing the queen, together with Kane, Sabrina and two of *Southerly Buster*'s officers carrying a large chest of trade goods, had returned to her palace and was staying there.

19

Captain Danzellan was in a bad temper.

He demanded, "Commander Grimes, why didn't you tell me that Drongo Kane was on this planet? I learned it, only by chance, from Lilian after you had left Melbourne—and then my radio officer monitored the conversation you had with your first lieutenant. . . ."

"To begin with," said Grimes tartly, "you didn't ask me. In any case, I gained the impression that you wanted nothing at all to do with me or my people." He was warming up nicely. "Furthermore, sir, I must draw your attention to the fact that the monitoring of Survey Service signals is illegal, and that you are liable to a heavy fine, and that your radio officer may have his certificate dealt with."

Danzellan was not awed. "A space lawyer!" he sneered.

"Yes, Captain. And a space policeman."

"Then why don't you arrest Kane?"

"What for?" asked Grimes. "He has broken no laws—Federation or local. I can neither arrest him nor order him off Morrowvia."

"Commander Grimes, I am paid to look after my owners' interests. I cannot do so properly while this man Kane is running around loose, corrupting the natives. To be frank, if you were not here I should feel justified in taking the law into my hands. Since you *are* here—I appeal to you, as a citizen of the Federation, for protection."

"Captain Danzellan, Captain Kane is cooking up some sort of deal with the natives. He, like you, is a shipmaster. *You* represent your owners, Kane *is* an owner. You allege that he is corrupting the natives and imply that he is queering your pitch. Meanwhile, *I* am wondering if whatever sort of deal *you* are cooking up will corrupt the natives. . . ."

"Of course not!" snorted Danzellan. "The Dog Star Line will always have their best interests at heart!"

"And the best interests of the management and shareholders . . . ?" put in Maggie.

Danzellan smiled in a fatherly way. "Naturally, Commander Lazenby. After all, we are businessmen."

"Mphm," Grimes grunted. He said, "Kane is a businessman too."

"But I was here first, Commander Grimes."

"*Lode Cougar* was here first, Captain Danzellan. Get this straight, sir—unless or until either you or Captain Kane steps out of line I am merely here as an observer."

"Then may I suggest, sir, that you start doing some observing? That is what I intend to do. I am going to call on Janine, now, to see if I can find out what line of goods Kane is peddling."

"I'll come with you," Grimes told him. "Maggie, you'd better come too. And you, Maya, if you wouldn't mind. Mr. Pitcher and Mr. Billard—stay by the pinnace."

The two men and the two women walked across the plaza to the main entrance of the palace. Four natives were standing in the doorway, spearmen of Janine's ceremonial bodyguard. They held their weapons not threateningly but so as to bar ingress.

"Let me pass!" huffed Danzellan.

"The queen insists on privacy," said one of the men.

"But I know Janine. We are good friends."

"The queen said, sir, that she and Captain Kane and her other guests were not to be disturbed."

Grimes nodded to Maya. Possibly she would be admitted while the offworlders were not. The Morrowvian woman walked forward until her breasts were pressing against the haft of one of the spears. She said indignantly, "You know who I am. Let me in!"

The spearman grinned. His teeth were sharp and very white. He said, "I am sorry, lady, but I cannot. Janine mentioned you especially."

"And what did she say?" demanded Maya.

"Do you really want to know, lady?" The man was enjoying this."

"Yes!"

"She said, lady, 'Don't let Commander Grimes or any other foreigners in here while I am in conference. And the same applies to that cat from Cambridge.' "

"Cat from Cambridge . . ." muttered Maya indignantly. "You can tell Janine that should she ever visit *my* town she will not be received hospitably."

"Well, Commander Grimes," asked Danzellan, "what are you doing about this?"

"What can I do?" countered Grimes irritably.

"We can talk things over," suggested Maggie Lazenby.

"Talk, talk!" sneered Danzellan, "while that damned pirate is raping a planet!"

"It's all that we can do at the moment," Grimes told him. "I suggest that we return to our pinnace. And I suggest that you, sir, do some talking."

"All right," said the shipmaster at last.

"The Dog Star Line's interest in this world will bring nothing but good to the people," stated Danzellan.

"Mphm," grunted Grimes skeptically.

"But it is so, Commander. If we are allowed to run things our way the planet will remain virtually unspoiled. There will be no pollution of the air, the soil or the seas. Unless the Morrowvians so desire it—and I do not think they will—there will be no development of heavy industries. The small luxuries that we shall bring in will demand power, of course—but solar power will be ample for their requirements."

"It all sounds very nice," admitted Grimes, "but what do your employers get out of it?"

"Oh, they'll make a profit—but not from the Morrowvians."

"From whom, then?"

"From passengers. Tourists. As you know, we have been, for many years, primarily freight carriers—but there is no reason why we should not break into the passenger trade, the tourist trade specifically. Trans-Galactic Clippers have been doing very nicely at it for some years now. But TG has the game sewn up insofar as the worlds on their itinerary are concerned.

"Now we, the Dog Star Line, have a new planet of our very own. We can build our own hotels and vacation camps, we can run cruises over the tropical seas in big schooners that we shall build and man— already recruiting for their crews is being opened on Atlantia." He smiled sympathetically at Maya. "I'm afraid that's necessary, my dear. Your people aren't very sea-minded."

"And you think that this scheme will work?" asked Grimes, interested.

"Why shouldn't it work, Commander? The advertising need only be truthful. Think of the posters, the brochures with photographs of all the beautiful, naked women—and, come to that, of the equally beautiful naked men. Visit Morrowvia—and shed your clothing, your cares, your inhibitions! Why, it'll have Arcadia licked to a frazzle!"

Maggie looked very coldly at Captain Danzellan. She said, "Arcadia is not a holiday resort for the idle rich, nor does it wish to be one. Our naturism is a way of life, not an advertising gimmick."

"Are you an Arcadian, Commander Lazenby? But what you said about naturism being a way of life on Arcadia applies equally well to Morrowvia. And we, the Dog Star Line, will do nothing to destroy that way of life. I have studied history, and I know how very often a superior race, a supposedly superior race, has ruined a simple people by forcing upon them unnecessary and unsuitable clothing. We shall not make that mistake."

"No, you won't," said Maggie. "It might affect your profits."

Grimes said, "I still think, Captain Danzellan, that you will ruin this world, whether or not you force the women into Mother Hubbards and the men into shirts and trousers."

Danzellan shrugged. "There's ruin *and* ruin, Commander Grimes. Which is the lesser of two evils—a flourishing tourist trade, or the introduction of heavy industry? Come to that—will the tourist trade be an evil?"

"And the tourists will *pay?*" asked Maya. "They will bring us things like the sun-powered cold boxes, and the clocks and the watches, and jewels like the ones that Captain Kane gave to Sabrina? Not that *I* want jewels," she added virtuously, "but I should like a cold box, and a clock that does not have to have the weights wound up every night."

"Maya is talking sense," said Danzellan.

"Yes, I am talking sense. You people have so many things to make life comfortable that we cannot make for ourselves, that we should not care to go to the trouble of making for ourselves. If offworlders are willing to pay for the pleasure of breathing our air, basking in our sunshine—then let them pay!"

"And there," said Danzellan smugly, "you have the attitude of a typical Morrowvian."

"But she's so simple," expostulated Grimes. "Her people are so simple."

Before Maya could answer Maggie stepped in. She said, "Perhaps not so simple, John. Apart from anything else, they have The History and Morrow's dictums to guide them. Too, there's an odd streak in their makeup. . . . I wish I knew . . ."

"I wish I knew what Kane was up to," said Danzellan.

"Don't we all," agreed Grimes.

20

They sat in the main cabin of *Seeker*'s pinnace—talking, smoking (even Maya tried one of Maggie's cigarillos and said that she liked it) and waiting for something to happen. Danzellan was in touch with his own ship by his wrist transceiver and also, of course, with Mr. Delamere, who had piloted *Schnauzer*'s boat to Ballarat and was remaining inside the craft. Grimes used the pinnace's radio to tell Mr. Saul what had happened so far and, meanwhile, all transceivers not otherwise in use were tuned to a variety of wavebands, in the hope that Drongo Kane's messages (if any) to *Southerly Buster* could be monitored.

At last Kane's voice sounded from Maggie's transceiver. He said simply, "Blackbird." The reply was almost immediate. "Pinnace to Captain. Blackbird." Then, "Pinnace to *Southerly Buster*. Blackbird." Finally, faintly, *"Southerly Buster* to pinnace. Acknowledge Blackbird."

"Blackbird?" echoed Grimes.

"I don't like it," said Maggie. "I don't like it. That word rings some sort of a bell. . . ."

"Captain to *Seeker*," said Grimes into the microphone of the main transceiver. "Captain to *Seeker*. Do you read me?"

"Loud and clear, Captain."

"That you, Mr. Saul? Keep your eyes open for any activities around *Southerly Buster*. Kane has just sent a message to his ship. It must be a code. Just one word. Blackbird."

"Blackbird . . ." repeated Saul. Then, "Have I your permission to use force?"

"What are you talking about, Saul?"

"Operation Blackbird, Captain. Didn't you know that blackbirding was a euphemism for slave trading?"

"He's right . . ." whispered Maggie. "And there are worlds where women such as these would fetch a good price—some of the Waldegren mining colonies, for example. . . ."

Grimes was thinking rapidly. If he departed at once it would be all of seven hours before he was back aboard *Seeker*. In seven hours a lot could happen. Saul, as second in command, was in full charge of the ship until her captain's return. Saul, normally, was a most reliable officer—but could Saul, with all his racial prejudices and bitternesses, be trusted to deal with the situation that was developing? Kane would scream to high heaven if a single shot were fired at his precious *Southerly Buster*, and he would not be the first pirate to have friends in high places—although heaven would not be one of them. Even so, if Kane were about to do something illegal he would have to be stopped.

The situation, Grimes realized, was made to order for Drongo Kane. *Seeker*'s captain was hours away from his ship—and so was *Southerly Buster*'s captain, but it didn't matter. The obnoxious Mr. Dreebly could embark the passengers, quote and unquote, and then lift ship into orbit, where Kane's pinnace could rendezvous with her. And once the Morrowvians were aboard the *Buster* she would be virtually untouchable insofar as hostile action by *Seeker* was concerned.

"Mr. Saul," ordered Grimes, "do all you can to prevent the natives from boarding *Southerly Buster*. Do not use arms unless there is absolutely no alternative. I am returning at once." He turned to Danzellan. "You heard all of that, Captain?"

"Of course, Commander."

"Good. Then I'll ask you to keep an eye on Drongo Kane for me."

"I'll do that, with pleasure."

Maggie said, "I'll stay with Captain Danzellan, John. I want to have another look at *Lode Cougar*'s records—if Janine will condescend to let me back into her palace after Kane has left. I have an idea that what I find may have some bearing on this situation. If it's what I'm afraid it might be—then be careful. Be bloody careful."

"I'll try," said Grimes.

"You always do, but . . ."

She followed Danzellan as the shipmaster returned to his own pinnace. Pitcher asked, "Take her up, sir?"

"Yes, Mr. Pitcher. And flog your horses. Put her

132

on a direct Great Circle; we've no time for sight-
seeing.''

While the navigator busied himself with charts
and instruments Billard did his best to make the
pinnace behave like a guided missile.

They wasted no time, screaming southward high
over the countryside, over the sea. Maya was awed,
a little frightened, even, and sat there in silence.
Pitcher and Billard exchanged occasional monosyl-
lables, while Grimes stuck to the transceiver. Timmins, the senior radio officer, was at the other end.
He reported, *"Southerly Buster* seems to be ready
for immediate lift-off, sir. All ports, have for the
main airlock, have been sealed.'' Then, a little later,
''Two officers have left the ship and are walking
toward the town of Oxford. Mr. Saul and Captain
Philby have followed them, with six Marines.''
Later still, ''Mr. Saul reports that the way was barred
to him and his party by a dozen spearmen and a
dozen archers. He is returning to the ship. I'll put
him on to you as soon as he's here.''

Grimes studied Saul's face in the tiny screen. The
man was struggling to repress his smoldering fury.
''Captain,'' he said, ''these damned people don't
want to be helped. They were there on the river bank,
with the spears and bows and arrows, and some
damned woman, the deputy queen she said she
was, ordered me back. She said, 'We don't want
you and the likes of you here. Captain Kane warned
Sabrina about you.' ''

''So . . .''

"So what are your instructions, Captain?"

"Get a boat out, to keep a watch over the town and to report what the people are doing. Have *Seeker* in a state of instant readiness for lift-off. . . ."

"I've already given the orders, sir. But the armament . . ."

"I've already told you not to go firing guns off indiscriminately. But . . . mphm. Have the belts for the sixty millimeters loaded with sleep gas shells. And if you use 'em—and you'll have to justify their use to me—make bloody sure that you don't *hit* anybody. Understood?"

"Understood, Captain."

"Good. Then keep me informed."

Grimes turned to Maya. "Can *you* tell me," he asked, what *is* going on?"

"I don't know. We have always kept ourselves to ourselves, Sabrina and I. We have never been close friends. We have never been friends. But Captain Kane gave many gifts to Sabrina's people. There were books, with beautiful pictures of other worlds, with accounts of other worlds. There were . . . catalogues, giving details of all the goods that may be purchased on other worlds. . . ."

"First Lieutenant to Captain." It was Saul again. "Number Three boat is in position over Oxford. We are trying to get a picture to you."

And there, on the screen, was the picture of the town as seen from the air. The boat was hanging almost directly over the central plaza and transmitting a magnified image. The two men from *Southerly Buster*, being clothed, were easily identifiable.

They were busily marshaling about two hundred Morrowvians into an orderly column. Even from above it was obvious that they were all women. To one side of the plaza a half dozen light handcarts had been loaded with possessions—cushions, pieces of pottery, longbows and quivers of arrows. One of Kane's men went to inspect the cart that was loaded with weapons, called a woman to him and was obviously telling her that these would have to be left. Then whoever was in charge of the boat got a long-range microphone working.

"I'm sorry, Peggy. These will have to be left behind."

"But the girls must have them, Bill. What will they do for sport on Caribbea if they have no bows?"

Caribbea? wondered Grimes. Probably it was the most glamorous world depicted in the brochures that Kane had distributed—but Essen would be a more likely destination for this shipment of female slaves.

"You can't use bows and arrows underwater," explained the man Bill patiently. "In the seas of Caribbea they use spear guns."

"But we don't *like* water. None of us likes water. Nobody will *make* us go into the water, will they?"

There's not much water on Essen, thought Grimes. *Only enough for washing and drinking—not that those Waldegren miners wash much, and they don't believe in diluting their schnapps. . . .*

"Nobody will *make* you do anything," lied Bill.

His companion called to him, "Dump that junk, and we'll get the show on the road!"

"Our ETA, Mr. Pitcher?" asked Grimes.

"We're doing the best we can, sir, but we can't make it before nineteen-hundred Local—another four and a half hours."

"Mr. Saul, do you read me?"

"Sir?"

"Lay a barrage of sleep gas on the bank of the river as soon as that column from Oxford gets under way."

"Very good, sir."

"And be *careful.*"

"Of course, sir." Saul's voice was hurt.

"Let me know as soon as you open fire, and give me a picture if you can."

"Very good sir." Grimes could almost read the first lieutenant's thoughts: *Get off my back, Whitey!*

It is not only the black races who hate slavery, thought Grimes, *and it is not only the black races who've been enslaved. But what the hell is Kane playing at? Pressing ahead with his blackbirding under the very nose of a Survey Service ship. . . . He's always prided himself on being able to keep just on the right side of the law.*

He said, "Get me Mr. Hayakawa, please."

"Yes, Captain?" asked the psionicist at last. His picture did not appear on the screen; that was being reserved for the transmissions from the lookout boat. "Yes, Captain?"

"Mr. Hayakawa, I know that your opposite number aboard the *Buster* is maintaining a block, but have you been able to pick up *anything?*"

"Yes, Captain. A few minutes ago there were stray thoughts from the mate of *Southerly Buster.*"

They ran like this, 'And the beauty of it is that the stupid Space Scouts can't touch us!' "

"That remains to be seen, Mr. Hayakawa," said Grimes. "That remains to be seen."

21

The trouble with radio as a means of communication is that anybody can listen. Grimes, in his later conversations with his ship, had employed a scrambler. He did not know whether or not *Southerly Buster* ran to a descrambling device. Apparently she did not. Dreebly appeared to be proceeding with his embarkation procedure as planned.

In an orderly march the two hundred young women streamed out of Oxford, a score of spearmen at the head of the column, another twenty male warriors bringing up the rear, behind the carts laden with small possessions. Kane's two men were in the lead. Grimes, remembering the general layout of the country, knew that once the van of the procession passed a low, tree-crowned hill it would be in the field of fire of *Seeker*'s guns. With an effort he restrained himself from taking over the fire control from Saul. He knew that a direct hit from a nonlethal gas shell can kill just as surely—and messily—as one from a high explosive projectile. But Saul was on the spot, and he was not. All he could do was to watch the marchers proceeding slowly along the bank of the winding river.

He heard Saul say quietly, "Bearing one hundred and seventy-five true. Range three thousand. Shoot."

"Bearing one hundred and seventy-five. Range three thousand. *Fire!*"

Even over the radio the hammering of the heavy automatics was deafening. Watching the screen Grimes saw a neat seam of explosions stitched across the line of advance of the Morrowvian women, saw the billowing clouds of greenish vapor pouring from each bursting shell.

"Traverse, traverse! Now—ladder!"

Nice gunnery, thought Grimes. Saul was boxing his targets in with the gas shells.

A new voice came from the transceiver. It was Dreebly's. *"Southerly Buster* to *Seeker*. What the hell are you playing at?"

"Seeker to *Southerly Buster*. What the hell are *you* playing at?"

Grimes decided that he had better intervene; Mr. Saul was not in a diplomatic mood. He said quietly, "Commander Grimes to *Southerly Buster*. What is the nature of your complaint, please?"

Dreebly spluttered, then, "What is the nature of my complaint, you ask? Some butterfly-brained ape aboard your ship is firing off guns. There're shells whistling past our control room."

"Routine weekly practice shoot, Mr. Dreebly," said Grimes. "Don't worry; we never hit anything unless we want to."

"But you're firing toward Oxford!"

"Are we? But our range setting is well short of the town."

"I know what you're firing at, Commander Grimes. You've a boat up, spotting for you!"

"What am I firing at, Mr. Dreebly?"

"Pah! You make me sick!" Dreebly broke off the conversation. Grimes returned his attention to the screen. The gas was slowly thinning, and through its translucent veil he could see the untidily sprawling figures of the Morrowvians—and of Kanes two officers.

Maya demanded, "You haven't killed them? You haven't killed them?"

"Of course not," Grimes told her. "They'll wake in a few hours' time, without even a headache. I've just put them to sleep, that's all. . . ."

Meanwhile Timmins had succeeded in tuning in to the conversation between Dreebly and Kane. Kane was saying, "Get them aboard, and then get off-planet! Yes, I *know* they can't walk—but you've ground cars, haven't you? And there are respirators in the stores. Pull your finger out, Dreebly, and get cracking! What do you think I pay you for?"

Saul was back on the air. "Sir, you heard all that. What do I do now?"

I could answer that question a lot more easily, thought Grimes, *if I knew that Kane was breaking Federation law. But he seems to have the idea that he is not. . . .*

"What do I do now?" repeated Saul.

"Mphm. Carry on with your practice shoot, Mr. Saul. Use H.E. Chew up the ground between *Southerly Buster* and the . . . er . . . intending emigrants."

140

"Emigrants! The *slaves*, you mean, Captain."

"They aren't slaves yet. Just make a mess of the terrain so that it's impassable to Kane's ground cars."

"But he's got boats, sir. He can use them."

"He has two boats—a pinnace, which is still at Ballarat, and one lifeboat. The lifeboat is just big enough for his crew. It will take it a long time to ferry two hundred people—especially as they will have to be lifted aboard it, and lifted off."

"I see, sir. . . . But what if *Southerly Buster* fires at us?"

"They won't dare, Mr. Saul. At least, I hope they won't. If they do—*if* they do—it is your duty to take every possible measure for the protection of *Seeker.*"

No, he thought, *Kane won't open fire, or order his mate to do so. Apart from anything else, he's the injured, innocent citizen and I'm the big, bad, gun-toting villain. I'm not happy about things at all, at all. But I* must *stop him.*

Meanwhile, he wished that he were back aboard his ship. He *liked* guns. He knew that this was childish of him, and that it was high time that mankind outgrew its love for noisy pyrotechnics. He knew that a gun pleads to be pointed at something—and then begs to have its trigger pulled. He hoped that Saul would remain content merely to wreck havoc on the landscape.

22

Saul wreaked havoc on the landscape. Grimes, watching on his screen, thought, relishing the play on words, *He's* wrecking *the landscape*. What had been grassland was now a crater-pitted desolation over which drifted acrid fumes, and the copses had been reduced to jagged, blackened stumps.

Kane came on the air. His voice, despite the fact that it had been relayed through at least two stations, was loud and clear. He said, "Commander Grimes, this is Captain Kane. My mate tells me that your first lieutenant's runnin' amok."

"Running amok, Captain Kane? What do you mean?"

"He's shootin off his guns—*your* guns—like a madman. Wastin' the taxpayer's money. He's interferin' with the embarkation of my passengers."

"Passengers, Captain Kane?"

"Yeah. Passengers. I own me own ship, an' if I decide to go into the passenger trade, that's my business."

"I'm sure it is, Captain. I'm sorry that my arrangements clashed with yours, but we were due for a practice shoot. . . ."

"Oh, you were, were you? An' did you promulgate a warnin'?"

"Unfortunately the facilities for so doing don't exist on this planet."

"Listen, Grimes, keep your nose out of my business or you'll get it bloodied."

"I'm inclined to think, Kane, that your business is *my* business. I represent the Federation. . . ."

"An' the Federation is supposed to encourage honest trade, not interfere with it."

"*Honest* trade?"

"You heard me. Honest *and* legal."

"All right, Kane. I have your word for it—for what it's worth. Where are you taking those women?"

"It's no concern of yours, Grimes. But it's only natural that after generations of isolation they'll want to see new worlds."

"Mphm. And how are they paying their fares? You never impressed me as being a philanthropic institution."

Kane laughed. "Have you never heard of *Travel Now, Pay Later?* TG Clippers do a lot of business that way, an' so does Cluster Lines."

"But these people don't have money."

"There're more important things in life than money—not that I can think of any right now."

Grimes realized that he was being talked into a corner. He said firmly, "I have to know where you intend taking your . . . er . . . passengers."

"I've already told you that it's none of your business."

"Would it be . . . Essen?"

"I'm not sayin' that is is—but what if it is Essen?"

"All right, Captain Kane. *If* you don't mind, I'll just assume that it is Essen. There'd be a good market there for women, wouldn't there? And Federation law definitely prohibits any kind of traffic in human beings."

"Yeah. It does. I know the law as well as you do, Commander. Probably better. An' I'm tellin' you flat that I'm breakin' no laws. So I'll be greatly obliged if you'll tell your Jimmy The One to get out of *my* mate's hair."

"I'm sorry, Captain Kane, but I just can't take your word for it."

"No, you wouldn't, would you? We couldn't have a spick-an'-span Survey Service commander takin' the word of Drongo Kane, a poor, honest workin' stiff, master of a scruffy little star tramp, could we? Oh, no. But I'll tell you this. One of your own officers, that Commander Maggie Lazenby, is in Janine's palace now, an' that stuffed shirt Danzellan is with her. Janine's lettin' 'em look at the *secret* records, the ones that she showed me. I'm not kiddin' you, Grimes. She'll tell you that you can't touch me."

"That remains to be seen, Captain Kane."

"Why don't you call her now?"

"Why not?" agreed Grimes tiredly. He got on to Timmins, ordered him to arrange a hookup. After a few minutes Maggie's voice came through the speaker of the pinnace's transceiver.

"Commander Lazenby here, *Seeker*."

"Stand by, please, Commander Lazenby. I'm putting you through to the captain."

"Captain here," said Grimes.

"Yes, John?"

"I've been talking with Captain Kane. . . ."

"Yes. I know. He's just come into the Records Room."

"He assures me that whatever he's doing is quite legal, and that you'll bear him out."

"Yes, but . . . I've just unearthed some very old records. . . . And from what Captain Danzellan tells me . . ."

"She says yes," put in Kane. "An' until the law is changed, if it ever is . . ."

"I said yes, *but* . . ." insisted Maggie.

"And if Tabitha is not lying . . ." contributed Danzellan.

"She said *yes!*" snapped Kane, his customary drawl forgotten.

"Maggie!" said Grimes forcibly. "Report, at once, in detail what you have discovered."

But there was no report. Kane used his wrist transceiver to jam the signals from those worn by Maggie and Danzellan, and before either or both of them could take any action the far more powerful transceiver of Kane's pinnace blocked all further transmissions from Ballarat.

23

Yes . . . *but.*
Yes . . . *but.*
But *what?*
Meanwhile, Mr. Saul had made the terrain between the landing site and Oxford quite impassable
to any ground vehicle, and would have to be restrained before he blew away all *Seeker*'s 60 mm
ammunition. Grimes told the first lieutenant to cease
fire, at once.

But what loophole in Federation law had Kane
discovered? What possible means of stopping that
loophole had Maggie discovered? Where did Francis
Delamere's local girlfriend, Tabitha, come into it?

Grimes decided that *Southerly Buster*'s lift-off
from Morrowvia must be, at the very least, delayed.
Could he stop the *Buster*'s boat from ferrying, a
dozen or so at a time, the unconscious women to the
ship? Yes, he could—but only at grave risk to the
boat's passengers. Embarkation would have to be
allowed to continue; by the time that it was complete
he, Grimes, would be back aboard *Seeker* and would
be able to take full charge.

Seeker's cannon were silent now, and *Southerly Buster*'s one remaining boat had nosed cautiously out of its bay and was flying to where the victims of the gas shell barrage were sprawled in the long grass. *Seeker*'s boat transmitted pictures of all that was going on. The small craft from the *Buster* dropped to a landing among the sleeping bodies and two men, wearing respirators, scrambled out of it. Working fast, they dragged fifteen of the women into the boat, careless of any abrasions or contusions they might inflict. They were equally careless with their two anesthetized mates—but that was no excuse. Kane's men were clothed and the risk of painful damage to their skins was so much less.

"Do I have to watch this, Captain?" the first lieutenant was raging.

"I'm afraid you have to, Mr. Saul," Grimes told him.

"Of course, if you can think of any way of stopping it without hurting any innocent people . . ."

Saul did not reply.

The first load was carried to *Southerly Buster*, the boat landing at the foot of the boarding ramp. Its passengers were dragged out and dumped on the ground, and almost immediately the boat began its return journey. Meanwhile a cargo hatch had been opened high on the side of the ship and the arm of a crane swung out. A net was lowered and the women, together with the two unconscious men, were piled into it, swiftly hoisted up an inboard. It was obvious that Kane was blessed with an efficient second-in-command.

Seeker's boat followed the one from *Southerly Buster* back to her loading site. There was a repetition of the callously efficient handling of the unknowing passengers—and then another, and then another.

But Grimes's pinnace had crossed the coastline now, was rushing inland. Grimes hoped to be back aboard *Seeker* before *Southerly Buster*'s embarkation was completed, although he could not hope to make it before sunset. Dusk was sweeping over the countryside as the two ships came into view, Kane's vessel towering brightly in the harsh glare of working lights. Saul had the hatch of the pinnace's bay open and waiting, and Billard expertly jockeyed the craft into the opening. Grimes was out through the door and running up to the control room before the pinnace had settled to her chocks. He found Saul staring sullenly out of a viewport.

"That's the last boatload," said the first lieutenant morosely. "Recall our our boat, sir?"

"Do just that, Mr. Saul. I want the ship buttoned up for lift-off."

"Yes. . . ." Saul gestured toward the *Buster*. "*She's* buttoning up."

The boom of the crane was withdrawn, the cargo hatch was shut. *Southerly Buster*'s boat lifted from the ground where she had discharged her last load, nosed up the mother ship's side to her bay. The ramp folded up and inward. The airlock door slid shut. Faintly there came the clangor of starting machinery, the unmistakable broken rhythm of the inertial drive.

Grimes ordered, "Use your sixty millimeters

again, Mr. Saul. Tracer, time fused. I want every shell bursting directly over her—not too close, but close enough so they can hear the shrapnel rattling around their control room.''

"Aye, sir!"

The automatics rattled deafeningly, the tracer streaked out from the muzzles in a flat trajectory, the bursting shells were spectacular orange flowers briefly blossoming against the dark sky.

Not at all surprisingly Dreebly's voice came screaming from the transceiver. "Stop firing! Stop firing, you idiots, before you hurt somebody!"

"Then shut down your engines!" commanded Grimes. "I am grounding you."

"By what authority? You have no authority here. This is not a Federated world."

"Shut down your engines!"

"I refuse."

Dreebly did more than merely refuse. Winking points of blue flame appeared from a turrent on *Southerly Buster*'s side. The streams of tracer from the two ships intersected, forming a lethal arch. Freakishly there were explosions at its apex at time-and impact-fused projectiles came into violent contact with each other—but the majority of *Seeker*'s shells still burst over *Southerly Buster*, and those from the *Buster*'s guns burst directly over *Seeker*.

"The bastard's hosepiping!" exclaimed Saul.

Yes, Dreebly was hosepiping, slowly and deliberately lowering the trajectory of his stream of fire. Would he have the nerve to fire at rather than over a

Federation ship? Grimes knew that *he* did not have the nerve to fire directly at *Southerly Buster*. Should he do so there would inevitably be casualties—and those casualties might well be among the *Buster*'s innocent passengers.

He said to Saul, "Cease fire."

"But, sir, I could put that turret out of action. . . ."

"I said, cease fire."

Seeker's hammering guns fell silent. There was a last burst from the *Buster*'s automatics, a last noisy rattle of shrapnel around *Seeker*'s control room. From the transceiver came Dreebly's taunting voice, "Chicken!"

"She's lifting," said Pitcher.

"She's lifting," echoed Saul disgustedly.

"Secure all," ordered Grimes, hurrying to the pilot's chair. "Secure all! There will be no further warning!"

He heard the coded shrilling of the alarms as he belted himself in. He checked the telltale lights on the control panel before him. By the time that the inertial drive was ready to lift *Seeker* clear of the ground *Southerly Buster* would be beyond pursuit range.

Was everything secure? It would be just too bad if it wasn't. The trained spacemen he could trust to obey orders promptly, the scientists were a different kettle of fish. But he couldn't afford to worry about them now, could not afford to indulge in the archaic, time-consuming, regulation ritual of the countdown.

He pushed the button for full emergency rocket

power—and almost immediately tons of reaction mass exploded from the venturis in incandescent steam. The giant hand of acceleration slammed him deep down into the padding of his seat. *Seeker* was lifting. *Seeker* was up and away, shooting skyward like a shell fired from some gigantic cannon. She overtook the slow-climbing *Southerly Buster*, roared past her as though she were standing still, left her well astern.

On the console the telltale light of the inertial drive was now glowing green. Grimes cut his rockets and the ship dropped sickening until the I.D. took hold, then brought up with a jar. She shuddered in every member as Grimes applied lateral thrust, as she lurched sideways across the sky. Pitcher, who had realized what the captain was trying to do, was doing, had stationed himself by the radar. "A little more, sir," he called. "Easy, now, easy. . . ." Then, "hold her at that!"

"Hold her!" repeated Grimes.

The ship shuddered and groaned again, but he was holding her in position relative to the ground below, to the still-climbing *Southerly Buster*. Then—slowly, but not so slowly as to conceal his intentions—he reduced vertical thrust. Dreebly tried, but in vain, to wriggle past *Seeker*. Grimes anticipated every move. (Later he learned that Hayakawa had been feeding him information, that Myra Bracegirdle, loyal rather to her sex than to her ship, had worked with and not against her fellow telepath.) It seemed that he could not go wrong—and every time that Dreebly attempted a lateral shift

Southerly Buster fell victim to the parallelogram of forces, inevitably lost altitude.

At last it was obvious to Mr. Dreebly that he had only two choices. Either he could return to the surface, or he could commit suicide by crushing his control room and everybody in it against *Seeker*'s far less vulnerable stern. He was not in a suicidal mood.

Grimes could not resist the temptation. He called for a microphone and for a hookup to the *Buster's* transceiver. He said just one word, and that with insufferable smugness.

"Chicken!"

Slowly the two ships dropped through the night—*Southerly Buster* cowed and inferior. Apart from that one taunt there had been no exchange of signals. Slowly they dropped, the defeated Dreebly and the overconfident Grimes.

It was this overconfidence that led, at the finish, to disaster. Just before Dreebly's landing Grimes miscalculated, and his stern made brief contact with the *Buster's* stem, doing her no great damage but throwing her off balance. With all his faults, Dreebly was a superb shiphandler. He fought to correct the topple, and had he not been inhibited by the ominous bulk of the other vessel hanging immediately above his control room he might well have done so. *Southerly Buster*'s fall was not completely catastrophic, but it was a fall, nonetheless. Visibly shuddering, she tilted, further and further, until her long axis was parallel to the ground.

It was then that Dreebly lost control, and there was a tinny crash as she dropped the last half meter.

24

It was, Grimes admitted glumly, quite a mess. Just how big a mess it was depended upon the legality or otherwise of his actions, the illegality or otherwise of Kane's operations. Legalities and illegalities notwithstanding, he was obliged to give assistance to the damaged—the wrecked—ship.

She was not a total write-off, although on a world with no repair yards it would be months before she could be made spaceworthy; she would probably have to be towed off-planet to somewhere where there were facilities. (And who would have to pay the bill? Kane would certainly take legal action against the Federation.)

Fortunately everybody aboard *Southerly Buster* had escaped serious injury, although the unfortunate women from Oxford, who had just been recovering consciousness at the time of the crash, were badly bruised and shaken. Them Grimes sent back to their town in *Seeker*'s boats.

He said to Saul, "I've done enough damage for one day. I'm turning in—for what's left of the night."

"The report to Base, sir. . . ."

Grimes told him coarsely what he could do to the report, then, "It will have to wait, Number One. I don't want to stick my neck out in writing until I have a few more facts."

"But you put down an attempt at slave trading, sir."

"Mphm. I hope so. I sincerely hope so. But I'm afraid that the bastard Drongo has some dirty big ace up his sleeve. Oh, well. Sufficient unto the day is the evil thereof. I'm getting some shut-eye. Good night, Number One."

"Good night, sir."

Grimes went up to his quarters. He paused briefly in his day cabin, poured himself a stiff drink, downed it in one swallow. He felt a little better. He went through into his bedroom, and stiffened with astonishment in the doorway, Maya was there, curled up on the bed, her back to him. She was snoring gently—and then immediately was wide awake, rolling over to face him.

"Maya . . ." he said reprovingly.

"I had to sleep somewhere, John," she told him, even more reprovingly. "And you seemed to have quite forgotten all about me."

"Of course I hadn't," he lied.

"Of course you had," she stated, without rancor. "But you had much more important things on your mind." She was off the bed now and was sagging enticingly against him. She said, in a very small voice, "And I was frightened. . . ."

The scent of her was disturbing. It was not unpleasant but it was strange—yet somehow familiar. It was most definitely female.

He said, "But you can't sleep here. . . ."

"But I have been sleeping here, John. . . ."

(So, she had begun to use his first name, too.)

She pleaded, "Let me stay. . . ."

"But . . ."

Her hands, with their strangely short fingers, were playing with the seal-seam of his shirt, opening the garment. They were soft and caressing on the skin of his back, but her nails were very sharp. The sensation was stimulating rather than painful. He could feel her erect nipples against his chest.

She pleaded again, "Let me stay. . . ."

Against his conscious will his arms went about her. He lowered his head and his lips down to hers. Oddly, at first she did not seem to understand the significance of this, and then she responded avidly. All of her body was against him, and all of his body was vividly aware of it. He walked her slowly backward toward the bed, her legs moving in time with his. Through the thin material of his shorts he could feel the heat of her thighs. She collapsed slowly, almost bonelessly, onto the nest that she had made for herself with pillows and cushions. He let her pull him down beside her, made no attempt to stop her as she removed the last of his clothing. (For a woman who had never worn a garment in her life she was learning fast.)

Their mating was short, savage—and to Grimes strangely unsatisfying. What should have been there for him was not there; the tenderness that he had come to expect on such occasions was altogether lacking. There was not even the illusion of love; this had been no more than a brief, animal coupling.

But she, he thought rather bitterly, *is not complaining.*

She was not complaining.

She, immediately after the orgasmic conclusion of the act, was drifting into sleep, snuggled up against him.

She was purring.

25

Dog tired, his nerves on edge after a sleepless night, Grimes stood in his control room and watched Drongo Kane come roaring in from the northward. He had been expecting Kane; Mr. Timmins had monitored the radio signals exchanged by Mr. Dreebly and his irate captain. He was expecting Maggie, too, but not for at least another hour. She had told him that Captain Danzellan was bringing her back to *Seeker*. She had refused to tell him what it was that she has discovered in the ancient records kept in Janine's palace, saying, "It will keep."

"Damn it all!" he had exploded, "I shall have Kane to deal with. And if what I suspect is true, legally I won't have a leg to stand on. Not unless *you* can pull a rabbit out of the hat."

"Not a rabbit," she told him. "Most definitely not a *rabbit*."

And that was all that he could get from her.

He had made use of the ship's memory bank encyclopedia facilities. In a Survey Service vessel these, of course, were continually kept up to date. He learned that although a committee was considering revisal, or even repeal, of the Non-Citizen Act this piece of legislation was still law. As far as he could see the act applied most specifically to the natives of Morrowvia—and that left him well and truly up the well known creek, without a paddle.

And here was Kane, dropping down from the morning sky, a man who knew Federation law so well that he could always bend it without actually breaking it. Here was Kane, a shipmaster *and* a shipowner who had learned that his vessel had been as good as (as bad as) wrecked by the officious actions of a relatively junior Survey Service officer. Here was Kane, more than a little annoyed about the frustration of his highly profitable activities.

Here was Kane.

Southerly Buster's pinnace slammed down alongside the parent ship in a flurry of dust and small debris. The door opened and Kane jumped out. He was no longer wearing his gaudy finery but had changed into utilitarian gray coveralls. Sabrina, still aglitter with jewelry, appeared in the doorway but Kane, irritably, motioned her back inside.

Dreebly, his head bandaged, came out of the ship. He stood there, drooping, while Kane obviously gave him a merciless dressing down. Then, slowly, the two men walked all around the crippled hulk, with the mate pointing out details of exterior damage. Grimes already knew what the damage was like inside—the Mannschenn Drive torn from its housing, the hydroponics tanks a stinking mess of shattered plastic and shredded greenery, most of the control room instruments inoperable if not completely ruined.

Saul came to stand by his captain's side. They watched as Kane and Dreebly clambered into the near-wreck through an amidships cargo hatch. The first lieutenant said happily, "You certainly put paid to *his* account, sir."

Grimes said, not so happily, "I only hope that he doesn't put paid to mine. . . ."

"But, sir, the man's a blackbirder, a slave trader! You've wrecked his ship—but that was the only way that you could stop the commission of a crime."

"Strong measures, Mr. Saul—especially if there were no crime being committed."

"But he fired on us, sir."

"At, not on. And we fired at him first."

"But he still hasn't a leg to stand on. . . ."

"Hasn't he? I've checked up on the Non-Citizen Act. I'm afraid that the Morrowvians do not qualify for citizenship. They have no rights whatsoever."

"I don't see it, sir. They're backward, I suppose—but they're as human as you or I."

"They're not," Grimes told him. "They're not, and that's the bloody trouble. What do you know of the Non-Citizen Act, Mr. Saul?"

"Not much, sir. But I can check up on it."

"Don't bother. I'll fill you in. That particular piece of legislation dates back to the bad old days when, briefly, the genetic engineers had far too much say. Although they were concerned primarily with the life sciences their outlook was that of engineers. You know, as well as I do, the peculiarities of the engineering outlook. If human beings and machines can't work together with maximum efficiency—then modify the human to suit the machine, not the other way round. A planet, like a house, is a machine for living in. If it is not suited to its intending occupants—then modify the occupants to fit. Then the generic engineers took things further. They manufactured, in their laboratories, androids—beings of synthetic flesh and blood that were, in effect, artificial men and women. Then they made 'underpeople'; the word was coined by a Twentieth Century science fiction writer called Cordwainer Smith and later, much later, used in actual fact. These underpeople were even less human than the androids, their very appearance making obvious their animal origins. They could not interbreed with true humans any more than the androids could—but they could breed, although they could not crossbreed. Put it this way—a dogman could mate with a dogwoman and fertilize her, or a catman with a catwoman. Only dogs—or ex-dogs—with dogs. Only cats—or ex-cats—with cats.

"Then there was the Android Revolt on Dancey. There was the virtual take-over of Tallis by the underpeople, although without bloodshed. The Federation Government put its foot down with a firm hand. No more androids were to be manufactured. No more underpeople were to be bred. All existing androids and underpeople were deprived of citizenship. And so on.

"It was quite some time before I realized the nature of the situation here, on Morrowvia. Kane, somehow, twigged it long before I did. But, last night, the final pieces of the jigsaw puzzle fell into place with a quite deafening *click*. I should have seen it before. There are so many clues. . . ."

"What do you mean, sir?"

"You did the science fiction course at the Academy, Mr. Saul."

"But I never cared for that wild stuff. I can't remember much of it."

"You must remember some of it. Anyhow, we all assumed that this planet was named after the captain of *Lode Cougar*. But I saw some of the records in the museum at Ballarat. Morrow was *not Lodge Cougar*'s master, neither was he one of her officers. He must have been one of the passengers—and a genetic engineer. I don't know yet how many survivors there were of *Lode Cougar*'s original complement when she landed, although Commander Lazenby will no doubt be able to tell us. I don't think that there could have been many. I don't think that there were any women of childbearing age among them. But, like all the ships of her period, she carried banks of fertilized ova—both human and animal. Perhaps the human ova had been destroyed somehow—or perhaps Morrow just didn't want to use them. Perhaps the ova of all the usual useful animals—with no exception—had been somehow destroyed—or perhaps Morrow was an aelurophile. I rather think that he was. He was also a science fiction addict—there are shelves of his books on display in the museum at Ballarat. He also had a rather warped sense of humor. The clues that he left!"

"What clues, sir?" asked Saul.

"In the names he gave—to the continent where *Lode Cougar* landed, to the four families that he . . . founded, to the planet itself. The planet of

Doctor Morrow . . . the island of Doctor Moreau. . . ."

"You're way beyond me, sir."

"Mr. Saul, Mr. Saul, you should have read that Twentieth Century rubbish while you had the chance. One of Morrow's books was *The Island of Doctor Moreau*, by a writer called Wells. Wells's Doctor Moreau was a rather mad scientist who converted animals into imitation humans by crude surgical means. Morrow . . . Moreau . . . see the connection? And one of the four family names on Morrowvia is Wells, another is Morrow.

"Another book was *The Planet Buyer*, by Cordwainer Smith. It was Cordwainer Smith who invented the underpeople. One of his favorite planets—he wrote, of course, before men had landed on Earth's moon—was Old North Australia, shortened to Norstrilia. So Morrow called the continent on which he landed North Australia, and made Cordwainer and Smith the other two family names.

"Meanwhile, he was having fun. He was breeding a people to fit in with all his own pet ideas. Evidently he disapproved of the nudity taboo, just as Commander Lazenby's people do on Arcadia. His political ideas bordered on anarchism. Possibly he was an anarchist. I seem to recall from my reading of history that there was quite a powerful, or influential, Anarchist Party on Earth, in both hemispheres, at the time of the Second Expansion. It worked underground, and it contributed to the decline and fall of the Russian Empire. And we see here the results of Morrow's ideas. Utterly unselfconscious nudism, no central government, no monetary system. . . .

"It's a pity that this Lost Colony was ever discovered. Its people are more human than many who are officially so—but they have no rights whatsoever."

There was a silence, then Saul said, "We, our people, know what it was like. . . ." Grimes looked at him rather nastily so he hastily changed the subject. "But tell me, sir, what did you mean when you said that the pieces of the puzzle fell into place last night?"

"You've served in *Pathfinder*, with Captain Lewis," said Grimes. "So have I. You know his taste in pets. You know how obvious it is, once you step inboard through the airlock. . . .

"Well, since you ask, my quarters stink of *cat*."

26

Maya joined the two men in the control room. She looked as though she had slept well. She glanced incuriously through the viewports at the disabled *Southerly Buster*, then said plaintively, "I'm hungry. . . ."

Go down to the galley and see if the cook can find you some fish heads . . . thought Grimes—and then despised himself for thinking it. He said, "Mr. Saul, would you mind taking Maya to the wardroom for breakfast?"

"But what does she *eat*, sir?" asked the first lieutenant desperately.

"I'll try anything, everything," she said sweetly, "until I find something I like."

Grimes watched her as she followed Saul out of the control room. There should have been, he thought, a tail ornamenting those shapely buttocks. A nice, furry, striped tail . . . He shrugged.

The officer of the watch reported, "Sir, an unidentified craft is approaching from the north."

"That will be *Schnauzer*'s pinnace," said Grimes. He went to the transceiver, selected the most probable waveband. "Commander Grimes to Captain Danzellan. Do you read me? Over."

"Loud and clear, Commander. Danzellan here. My ETA your landing site is thirty minutes Standard, twenty-four minutes Local, from now. I have your Commander Lazenby with me. Over."

"Thank you, Captain Danzellan." Should he ask to speak with Maggie? No. She had made no attempt to speak with him. And Grimes was in a misogynistic mood. *Women! Cats!*

He returned to the viewport. He passed the time by mentally composing the sort of report—or complaint—that he would write if he were Drongo Kane.

To: Flag Officer in Charge of Lindisfarne Base
From: Drongo Kane, master and owner of s/s
   Southerly Buster
Subject: Piratical action by Lieutenant Commander
   John Grimes, Captain of ESS Seeker.
Sir,
   I regret to have to report that while my vessel was proceeding on her lawful occasions she was wantonly attacked by your Seeker, *under the command of your Lieutenant Commander Grimes. Commander Grimes not only used his armament to impede the embarkation of fare-paying passengers, subjecting them to a sleep gas barrage, but also fired upon* Southerly Buster *herself. Later he attempted to ram my ship after she had lifted off, and only the superlative skill of my chief officer, who was in charge of the vessel at the time, averted a collision. Although*

*contact between the two ships was avoided contact
with the ground was not. As a result of this*, Southerly Buster *sustained severe structural damage.* . . .

"Pinnace in sight visually, sir," reported the
O.O.W.

"Thank you, Mr. Giles."

Danzellan came in more slowly and cautiously
than Kane had done, but he wasted no time, setting
his craft down at the foot of *Seeker*'s ramp. Grimes
watched *Schnauzer*'s master get out, then help Maggie Lazenby to the ground. He told Giles to telephone down to the airlock sentry, instructing the
man to inform Captain Danzellan and Maggie that he
would be waiting for them in his quarters. He went
down to his day cabin, hastily shutting the door
between it and his bedroom. The smell of cat was
still strong.

He found and filled his foulest pipe, lit it. When
Danzellan and Maggie came in he was wreathed in
an acrid, blue smog.

"What a fug!" she exclaimed.

The intercom telephone buzzed. It was the
O.O.W. calling. "Sir, Captain Kane and his chief
officer are at the airlock. They wish to speak to
you."

"Send them up," said Grimes.

"What in the universe have you been *doing*,
Commander?" asked Danzellan. "Fighting a small
war?"

"Or not so small," commented Maggie.

"I," Grimes told them bitterly, "was attempting

to prevent the commission of a crime. Only it seems that slave trading is not a crime, insofar as this bloodly world is concerned."

"The underpeople . . ." said Maggie softly. "Underpeople—and the still unrepealed Non-Citizen Act. . . . But how did you find out? It took me hours after I was able to get my paws on the records. . . ."

"I added two and two," Grimes told her, "and came up with three point nine recurring. All the clues are so obvious. Rudimentary nipples, paw-like hands and feet, the way in which the people eat and drink, and the use of 'cat' as a term of opprobrium when, apart from the Morrowvians themselves, there isn't a single animal of Terran origin on the planet. . . ."

Danzellan grinned. "I see what you mean. I've been known to refer to particularly stupid officers as 'pathetic apes.' "

"Those same points had *me* puzzled," admitted Maggie. "But I'm surprised that *you* noticed them."

"And Morrow's books," went on Grimes. *"The Island of Doctor Moreau.* The Cordwainer Smith novels. The names of the four families—Wells, Morrow, Cordwainer and Smith. And North Australia. . . ."

"You're losing me there," admitted Maggie.

A junior officer knocked at the door. "Captain Kane to see you, sir. And Mr. Dreebly."

Kane blew into the room like the violent storm after which his ship was named. He blustered, "I'll have your stripes for this, Grimes! As soon as your bloody admiral hears my story he'll bust you right down to Spaceman Sixteenth Class—unless he decides to shoot you first!''

"Slave trading," said Grimes, "is prohibited by Federation law."

"Yeah. It is. But, Mr. Commander Grimes, such laws exist only for the protection of Federation citizens. The Morrowvians are non-citizens."

"How do you make that out?"

"How do I make that out? Because they're under-people, Commander—which means that they have the same status as androids, which means that they have no bloody status at all. They're no more than cattle—with the accent on the first syllable!" He laughed briefly at his own play on words, turned to glare at Dreebly when he essayed a snicker. "The only protection they can claim is that of the S.P.C.A.—and there's no branch of that society on Morrowvia!"

Grimes looked at Maggie appealingly. She flashed him a fleeting smile of encouragement. He looked at Danzellan. The portly shipmaster winked at him.

"Slavery," said Grimes firmly, "is still a crime, ethically if not legally."

"So is piracy, Grimes. Ethically *and* legally."

"I seem to recall past occasions in your own career. . . ."

"We're not talking about them. We're talking about *this* occasion in *your* career. The unprovoked attack upon an innocent merchantman. To begin with, Grimes, you can place your artificers at my disposal. *If* they make a good job I just might tone my report to your bosses down a little." He laughed lightly. "A stiff note on paper, instead of a stiff note on cardboard. . . ."

"Mphm," grunted Grimes thoughtfully.

"In fact, Commander," went on Kane, speaking quite quietly now, his exaggerated accent gone, "I think that you could help me considerably. . . ."

And Kane, thought Grimes, *owes his survival to the number of friends he has in high places. And Kane is an opportunist. For all he knows I might be an admiral myself one day. He's debating with himself, "Shall I put the boot in, or shall I let bygones be bygones?" Too, he's probably not* quite *sure if he* is *altogether in the right, legally speaking. . . .*

"Don't trust him, Commander," said Danzellan.

"Keep your nose out of this!" snarled Kane.

"*I* discovered this planet," stated Danzellan. "The Dog Star Line . . ."

". . . can go and cock its leg against a lamp post," Kane finished the sentence.

"Gentlemen," said Grimes soothingly. "Gentlemen. . . ."

"I can't see any round here," remarked Maggie.

"You shut up for a start," he told her. But he realized that her flippancy had broken the tension.

"What do you say, Commander?" persisted Kane. "You have a workshop, and skilled technicians. . . . Get the old *Buster* back into commission for me and you can write your own report to your superiors." He grinned. "After all, I'm just a semiliterate tramp skipper. Paperwork's beyond my capabilities."

"And what about me?" asked Danzellan interestedly.

"The Dog Star Line's big enough to look after itself, Captain, as I have no doubt that it will. My own activities, for quite some time, anyhow, will be confined to this continent of New England. You," he said generously, "can have North Australia."

"Thank you, Captain. I appreciate the gesture. But I feel obliged to tell you that my employers are not quite the soulless bastards that they have often been alleged to be. They would not wish to share a planet with a slaver. Not," he added, "that it will ever come to that."

"So you're pulling out?" asked Kane.

"No."

"I warn you, Captain Danzellan, that if you or your people try to make things awkward for me, I shall make things even more awkward for the Dog Star Line. They'll finish up by buying me out, at my price. It will not be a low one." He turned to Grimes. "And what do you say, Commander, to my proposition to you?"

"No," said Grimes. "No, repeat no."

"You'll be sorry. My report—and it's a damning one—has already been written. My Carlotti transmitter is quite powerful, and will be able to raise the Lindisfarne Base station with ease. You'd better have your letter of resignation ready."

He turned to go.

"Hold your horses," said Maggie sweetly. "Hold your horses, Captain Kane. I haven't said *my* party piece yet."

27

She said, "You'd better all sit down and make yourselves comfortable, as this is quite a long story. You, John, just read the very beginnings of it. You, Captain Kane, read enough to convince you that slaving activities, with Federation law as it stands at present, would be quite legal. And I was able to do more research than either of you.

"The story of *Lode Cougar* is not, in its early stages, an unusual one. There was the gaussjammer, lifting from Port Woomera, bound for the newly established colony on Austral—*your* home world, Captain Kane. As well as the intending colonists she carried cargo, among which was a shipment of fertilized ova. Dogs were required on Austral, and cats, to deal with the numerous indigenous vermin. There were cattle too, of course, and horses—oh, all the usual. And there were human ova, just in case the ship got thrown off course by a magnetic storm and had to start a new colony from scratch, in some utterly uncharted sector of the galaxy. Quite a number of colonies were started that way.

"*Lode Cougar* was unlucky—as so many of the

old gaussjammers were. A magnetic storm threw her thousands of light-years off course. Her navigators were unable to determine her position. Her pile was dead, and her only source of power was her diesel generators. The engineers kept these running—which meant that the ship's biochemist was having to produce fuel for the jennies rather than food for the crew and passengers.

"But all they could do was to stand on and stand on, from likely star to likely star, pulling their belts ever tighter, finding that some suns had no planetary systems, that other suns had worlds in orbit about them utterly incapable of supporting any kind of life, let alone life as *we* know it.

"Almost inevitably there was a mutiny. It came about when a gang of starving passengers was caught foraging in the cargo spaces—*the refrigerated cargo spaces*. Is it cannibalism when you gorge yourself on fertilized human ova? A rather doubtful legal point. . . . Anyhow, the master of the *Cougar* decided that it was cannibalism, and ordered the offenders shot. In the consequent flareup there was rather too much shooting and then an orgy of *real* cannibalism. . . . Things went from bad to worse after that, especially since the captain, his senior officers and most of the more responsible passengers were killed. Among the survivors was a professional genetic engineer, a Dr. Edward Morrow. He wrote despairingly in his private journal, 'Will this voyage never end? Men and women are behaving like wild beasts. No, I must not say that, because my fellow passengers are worse than beasts. No decent animal could ever sink to such depths.' That passage sticks in my memory. It explains so much. Some time later he wrote that the ship was approaching yet another sun, and that Bastable, the liner's third officer, hoped that it would run to a habitable planet. 'If it does not,' Morrow wrote, 'that is the finish of us. Soon there will be only one survivor, gnawing the last shreds of human flesh from the last bone.'

"*Lode Cougar* cautiously approached the world that was still to be named. It looked to be habitable. There was a meeting of crew and passengers—what was left of them—and Bastable told them that the landing would have to be made in high magnetic latitudes, for the obvious reason. The others told Bastable that the landing would have to be made in some region with a hospitable climate; nobody was in fit condition to undertake a long trek over ice fields. Bastable acceded to their demands, after a long argument. Had he not been the only man capable of handling the ship he would have been murdered there and then.

"He got her down, as we know. He got her down, in one piece. The experience shattered him. He went to his quarters immediately after the landing, got out the bottle of alcohol that he had been jealously hoarding, and drank himself into insensibility. In his weakened condition—like all the rest he was more than half starved—it killed him. Regarding his death, Morrow made more unkind remarks in his journal about the human race.

"With the very few survivors a colony of sorts could have been started, might possibly have survived. There were ten men—nine of them, including Morrow, passengers, one of them a junior engineer. There were six women, four of them young. Morrow persuaded his companions that they would have a far better chance if they had underpeople to work for them. The only ova that had survived the trouble were those of cats—but Morrow was expert in his profession. With the aid of the engineer he was able to set up incubators and then—all that was required was in the ship's cargo—a fully equipped laboratory.

"He wrote again in his journal, 'The first batch is progressing nicely, in spite of the acceleration. I feel . . . paternal. I ask myself, why should these, my children, be *under*people? I can make them more truly human than the hairless apes that may, one day, infest this new world. . . .'

"Regarding the deaths of his fellow *Lode Cougar* survivors he says very little. One suspects that he knew more than he wrote about the food poisoning that killed Mary Little, Sarah Grant and Delia James. One wonders if Douglass Carrick fell off that cliff, or was pushed. And how did Susan Pettifer and William Hume come to get drowned in the river? It is interesting to note, too, that Mary, Sarah, Delia and Susan were the potential childbearers. And, as well as working in his laboratory, Morrow set up a still and soon had it in operation, turning out a very potent liquor from a fermented mash of berries and wild grain. The surviving men and the two remaining women didn't care much then what happened, and as Morrow had succeeded in activating a team of robots from the cargo he was independent of them.

He didn't bother to kill them as his first batch of 'children' was growing to forced maturity. He just let them die—or be killed by wild animals when they went out hunting for meat.''

"Yes," said Kane. "I know all that. The Morrowvians are non-citizens.''

"I haven't finished yet, Captain Kane. There was something of the Pygmalion in Morrow—as there must have been in quite a few of those genetic engineers. He fell in love with one of his own creations—his Galatea. He even named her Galatea.''

"Touching . . .'' commented Kane.

"Yes, wasn't it? And he married her; he'd decided that his people couldn't live in a state of complete anarchy, and must have a few, necessary laws. So he made the union legal.''

"Uncommonly decent of him,'' sneered Kane.

"But that didn't stop him from having quite a few concubines on the side. . . .''

"So the Morrowvian idol had his feet of clay.''

"Don't we all, Captain, don't we all?''

"So the records prove that true humans can have sexual relations with these underpeople. I'd found that out long before I saw the precious records. Judging by the stink in here, Commander Grimes has found it out too.''

"John! What have you been doing? Don't tell me that you and Maya . . .''

"I won't tell you if you tell me not to.''

"So you did. I hope you enjoyed it, that's all.''

Kane laughed patronizingly. "So I'll leave you people to your family squabbles, and get back to my ship and send my report off to Lindisfarne. A very good day to you all."

"Wait!" Maggie snapped sharply. "I haven't finished yet."

"I don't think that anything further you can say will change my mind. Underpeople are underpeople. Underpeople are property. Period."

"There is a ruling," said Maggie slowly, "that any people capable of fertile union with true people must, themselves, be considered true people."

"And so, to coin a phrase, what?"

"Morrow's unions were fertile."

"So he says. How many glorified tomcats were sneaking into his wife's or his popsies' beds while he was elsewhere?"

"The Morrow strain is strongest in North Australia, among the people who bear his name."

"What evidence is there?"

"The Morrows are a little more 'human' than the other Morrowvians. Very few of their women have supplementary nipples. Their general outlook is more 'human'—as you know yourself. That show you put on for Janine with the saluting cannon. . . . And the show she put on for us."

"Yeah. I grant you that. But I think the words of the ruling you mentioned are, 'a fertile, *natural* union.' Old Doc Morrow was a genetic engineer. I've heard it said that those boys could crossbreed an ant and an elephant. . . . I'm sorry. I'm really sorry for you all. You've tried hard, but by the time the Federation reaches a decision I'll have made my pile."

"I," said Danzellan, "can supply more proof for Commander Lazenby's arguments."

"You, Captain? You're no biologist, you're just a shipmaster like myself."

"Even so. . . ." The master of *Schnauzer* was obviously finding something highly amusing. "Even so. . . . You know, it's just over two hundred and twenty days that I first landed on Morrowvia—and that's about two hundred and seventy days Standard. . . ."

"I can do sums in my head as well as you can."

"I am sure you can, Captain Kane. And are you married? Have you a family?"

"No—to both questions."

"It doesn't matter. Well, on the occasion of my first visit, my second officer, Mr. Delamere, got Tabitha, the daughter of the Queen of Melbourne, into trouble, as the saying goes. The young idiot should have taken his contraceptive shots before he started playing around, of course. He's really smitten with her, and managed to get himself appointed to *Schnauzer*, rather against my wishes. Now he wants to make an honest woman of the girl—once again, as the saying goes—but Lilian, Tabitha's mother, will not allow him to marry her unless he complies with local law. This means that he will have to change his name to Morrow, which he does not want to do. He will, of course. The Dog Star Line wants a resident agent on this planet. And even though the queenships are not hereditary in theory they usually are in practice."

"What are you driveling about?" asked Kane crudely.

Danzellan flushed. He said stiffly, "Tabitha has presented young Delamere with a son."

"And how many local boyfriends has she had?" demanded Kane.

"She says that she has none. Furthermore, I have seen the baby. All the Morrowvians have short noses—except this one, who has a long nose, like his father. The resemblance is remarkable. . . ."

Kane refused to concede defeat.

"Paternity tests . . ." he mumbled.

"I can soon arrange those, Captain," Grimes told him. "Don't forget that I have my own biologists, as well as other scientists." He turned to Danzellan. "Did Mr. Delamere come with you, Captain? Call him up, and we'll wet the baby's head!"

"You can break a bottle of champagne over it!" growled Kane, pushing his way out of the day cabin, brushing past Maya who was just coming in, and complaining, "I'm *still* hungry, John. They say that all the ice cream is finished. . . ."

"Go on," said Maggie. "Do the decent thing. Buy the girl a popsicle to show her how much you love her."

"I'll have some more ice cream made, Maya," promised Grimes, looking at her with combined pity and irritation, noticing that Danzellan was regarding her with condescending amusement.

The Morrowvians, thanks to the long-dead Morrow's skill—he had even imposed the right gestation period on his people—were safe from Drongo Kane and his like, but had no defenses against Big Business as represented by the Dog Star Line.

Or had they?

Grimes suspected that they, with their innate feline charm combined with selfishness, would not do at all badly in the years to come.

GATEWAY TO
NEVER

A. BERTRAM CHANDLER

ace books
A Division of Charter Communications Inc.
A GROSSET & DUNLAP COMPANY
360 Park Avenue South
New York, New York 10010

Copyright © 1972 by A. Bertram Chandler

An ACE Book
This Ace printing: June 1978

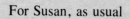

For Susan, as usual

1

Commodore John Grimes did not like Customs Officers; to his way of thinking they ranked with, but even below, Tax Collectors. The Tax Collector, however, is loved by nobody—with the possible exceptions of his wife and children—whereas the Customs Officer makes his impact only upon the traveling public, among whom professional spacemen are numbered.

Grimes was not at all pleased when his latest secretary, Miss Pahvani, told him that the Port Forlorn Chief of Customs wished to see him. It was not that he was especially busy; the only thing to occupy his attention was the Stores Requisition sent in by the Chief Officer to *Rim Mandrake*, through most of the items on which he had been happily running his blue pencil.

He looked up from his desk and said irritably, "Tell him I'm busy."

Miss Pahvani treated him to her impersonation of a frightened fawn. "But, sir, he says that it is important. And he is the Chief Collector."

"And I'm the Chief Astronautical Superintendent

of Rim Runners. *And* the Officer allegedly Commanding the Rim Worlds Naval Reserve.''

''But, sir, he is waiting.''

''Mphm.'' Miss Pahvani's brother, Grimes recalled, was a Junior Customs Inspector. How did a pretty girl like this come to have a near relative in a profession like that? ''All right,'' he said. ''Show him in.''

And what was it this time? Grimes wondered. There had been the flap when an overly zealous searcher had discovered that the Master of *Rim Basilisk* had no less than two bottles of duty-free gin over and above his allowance for personal consumption. There had been the unpleasantness about the undeclared Caribbean cigars in the cabin of *Rim Gryphon's* Third Officer. And what was he, Grimes, supposed to do about it? Send this-practice-must-cease-forthwith Circulars to all ships, that was what. . . . He imagined that he was a Rim Runners' Master (as he had been, before coming ashore) and mentally composed a letter to himself as Astronautical Superintendent. *Dear Sir, Your Circular Number so-and-so is now before me. It will shortly be behind me. Yours faithfully.* . . .

''Ah, Commodore,'' said Josiah Billinghurst, the Chief Collector of Customs, breaking into his thoughts.

''Mr. Billinghurst.'' Grimes got to his feet, with an outward show of cordiality. After all, he had to share the spaceport with this man. ''Come in, come in. This is Liberty Hall; you can spit on the mat and call the cat a bastard!''

Billinghurst winced, as he was intended to do;

Grimes knew very well that he hated the merest suggestion of coarse language. He lowered his bulk into one of the chairs on the other side of Grimes' big desk. He was a grossly fat man and his gold-braided uniform did not become him, and neither did he become the uniform. Grimes wondered, as he had wondered many times before, what perverted genius had first thought of putting these enemies of mankind into naval dress.

"Coffee, Mr. Billinghurst?"

"If I may, Commodore."

Miss Pahvani brought in the tray, poured for the two men. *One more smile like that,* Grimes thought sourly, *and our fat friend will make your brother a Chief Inspector.* He said, when the girl was gone, "And what can I do you for?"

"Nothing, I hope." Billinghurst permitted himself an apology for a smile, then reverted at once to the appearance of a mournful overfed bloodhound. "But you might be able to do something for me."

"In which of my official capacities?" asked Grimes.

"Both, quite possibly." He sipped noisily from his cup. "This is good coffee."

"Imported. And the duty was paid on it."

"I have no doubt that it was. Frankly, Commodore, it wouldn't worry me much if it were out of ship's stores and not a cent of duty paid."

"You surprise me, Mr. Billinghurst."

Billinghurst sighed. "All you spacemen are the same. You regard us as your natural enemies. Do you think that I get any pleasure from finding one of your junior officers for minor smuggling?"

"That thought had flickered across my mind," said Grimes. "But tell me, who's been naughty now? *Rim Mandrake*'s the only ship in port at the moment. I hadn't heard that any of her people had been guilty of the heinous crime of trying to take an undeclared bottle of Scotch ashore."

"None of them has, Commodore."

"So?"

"I don't make the laws, Commodore Grimes. All that I'm supposed to do is enforce them. The government decides what duty shall be paid on the various imported luxuries, and also what quantities of which commodities may be brought in, duty-free, by passengers and ships' crews. Regarding this latter, you know as well as I do that we are inclined to be lenient."

Reluctantly Grimes agreed.

"When something, such as liquor or tobacco, is intended for personal consumption only, we often turn a blind eye. When something is smuggled ashore to be sold at a profit, we pounce."

"Mphm."

"And then, Commodore, there are the prohibited imports. You have traveled widely; you know that on many worlds drugs of all kinds are regarded as we regard tobacco and alcohol, or tea and coffee, even."

"Francisco . . ." contributed Grimes.

"Yes, Francisco. A planet of which I have read, but which I have no desire ever to visit."

"An odd world," said Grimes. "Religion is the opium of about half of the people, and opium is the religion of the other half."

"Neatly put, Commodore. Now, I need hardly tell you that drugs, especially the hallucinogens, are banned on the Rim Worlds."

"We get along without them."

"You do, Commodore, and I do, but there are some who think that they cannot. And where there is a demand there will soon be a supply."

"Smuggling?"

"Yes."

"How do you know it is smuggling? How do you know that somebody miles from any spaceport hasn't a mushroom plot, or that somebody with more than a smattering of chemistry isn't cooking up his own LSD?"

"We are working closely with the police in this matter, Commodore. All the evidence indicates that drugs are being smuggled in."

"And what am I supposed to do about it? I'm neither a Customs Officer nor a policeman."

"You are in a position of authority. Your captains are in positions of authority. All that I ask is a measure of cooperation."

"It is already laid down in Company's Regulations," said Grimes, "that the penalty for smuggling is instant dismissal."

"The penalty for being *caught* smuggling," said Billinghurst.

"Isn't that the same thing?"

"It's not, and you know it, Commodore."

"All right. I'll compose a Circular on the subject."

"I expected more from you than this, Commodore Grimes."

"What more *can* I do?" Then, "And how do you know it's *our* ships? Most of them are running the Eastern Circuit, and to the best of my knowledge and belief no drugs are grown or manufactured on Tharn, Mellise, Stree or Grollor, any more than they are on Lorn, Faraway, Ultimo or Thule."

"*Rim Dingo*," said the Chief Collector, "is engaged in the trade between Lorn and Elsinore. Drug addiction is no problem on that world, but ships from all over the Galaxy come into the ports of the Shakespearean Sector. *Rim Wombat* runs mainly to Rob Roy, in the Empire of Waverley. As long as the Waverleyans get their Scotch they don't want anything else—but the Waverley ports are open to Galactic trade."

"Mphm. But I still can't see why there should be all this fuss about mind-expanding chemicals that can be purchased openly on at least a thousand planets."

"Here," stated Billinghurst, "their use is illegal."

"If people enjoy something," said Grimes, "make a law against it. Who was it who said that the law was an ass?"

"I don't like your attitude, Commodore Grimes," Billinghurst said reprovingly.

"There are times when I thoroughly disapprove of myself," said Grimes, with mock penitence. "Anyhow, I'll get that Circular into production."

"Thank you," said Billinghurst. "I'm sure that it will be a great help."

Sarcastic bastard! thought Grimes.

2

That evening he talked things over with his wife. He said, "That fat slob Billinghurst was in to see me."

"What have you done now?" Sonya asked him.

"Nothing," replied Grimes, hurt.

"Then what have your captains and officers been doing?"

"Nothing, so far as I know."

"Our Mr. Billinghurst," she said, "doesn't like you enough to drop in for a social chat."

"You can say that again." The Commodore's prominent ears reddened. "I don't like him, either. Or any of his breed."

"They have their uses," she said.

Grimes looked at Sonya in a rather hostile manner. He growled, "You *would* say that. After all, you are an Intelligence Officer, even if only on the Reserve List."

"Why rub it in?" she asked.

"I'm not rubbing anything in. I'm only making the point that Customs Officers and Intelligence Officers have a lot in common."

"Yes, we do, I suppose. To be in either trade you

have to be something of a human ferret. And the Survey Service's Intelligence Branch has worked with the Customs authorities more than once."

"Has Billinghurst asked you to work with him?" he demanded.

"No. Of course not. He represents the Government of the Confederacy, and my Reserve Officer's Commission is held, as well you know, in the Federation's Survey Service."

"You are a citizen of the Confederacy by marriage."

"Yes, but a private citizen. As far as the Rim Worlds are concerned I'm just a civilian. Of course, if I got orders from my bosses on Earth to work with Billinghurst—just as I've had orders in the past to work with you—I should do just that."

"Mphm. Well, I most sincerely hope that you don't."

"Suppose," she suggested, "that you tell me what all this is about. I know you don't like Billinghurst—but he's only doing the job that he's paid to do."

"Why should the taxpayers be forced to pay for the upkeep of their natural enemies?" asked Grimes rhetorically.

"It always has been so," she told him. "It's just one of the prices one pays for civilization. But suppose you put me in the picture insofar as you and Mr. Billinghurst are concerned."

"All right. As you know very well the Rim Worlds are far less permissive than Earth and the older colonies. By comparison with them, we're practically puritanical."

"Are we? I haven't noticed anybody suffering agonies of repression."

"Perhaps not. But just compare our attitude towards the commoner drugs with that of, say, Earth. On the home planet marihuana can be purchased as openly as tobacco. Here, on the Rim, it is banned. There the more potent hallucinogens can be bought by those who have a license to use them—even that Dew of Paradise they distill on Arrid. Here, they are banned. I could go on. . . ."

"Don't bother. So somebody's been drug running, and Billinghurst thinks that it's your boys. Right?"

"Right."

"And he wants you to do something about it. Right?"

"Right."

"And what are you doing about it?"

"I've already done it. I've composed a this-practice-must-cease-forthwith Circular, addressed to all Masters and Chief Officers, drawing their attention to Rule No. 73 in Rim Runners' Regulations—the instant dismissal if caught smuggling one."

"And do you think that will be enough?" she asked.

"That's the least of my worries," he said.

"At times—and this is one of them—I find your attitude towards things in general rather hard to understand." Her slender face was set in severe lines, her green eyes stared at him in what could have been accusation.

Grimes squirmed slightly. He said firmly, "I am

not, repeat not, a Customs Officer—and for that I thank all the Odd Gods of the Galaxy. Furthermore, ever since man came down from the trees he has needed an assortment of drugs—tea, coffee, alcohol, tobacco, the juice of sacred mushrooms, the smoke from burning Indian hemp—to take the rough edge off things in general. Most—all, probably—of these things are dangerous if taken in excess. So are plenty of non-drugs. After all, you can kill yourself overeating."

"Talking of that," she said sweetly, "you could stand to lose a pound or three . . . or four . . . or five."

He ignored this. "What Billinghurst is doing is interfering with the most sacred freedom of mankind."

"Which is?"

"Freedom to go to hell your own way. The odd part is that in any culture where this freedom is an undeniable right very few people take advantage of it. But once the law, in its wisdom, says, "You *must* be good," it's a different story. You will recall that Atlantia, only a few years ago, tried to ban the consumption of alcohol. As a result non-drinkers became drinkers, moderate drinkers became heavy drinkers, and those who had been heavy drinkers drank themselves into early graves. And the rum runners made their fortunes."

"Yes," she said, "the rum runners made their fortunes. People like Drongo Kane, who has always ranked high on your list of pet dislikes. And now that some genius has discovered that there's an ideal market for drugs out on the Rim there'll be more fortunes made, and all by the dregs of humanity. Tell me, John, if you knew that Drongo Kane was among the runners would you be content to do no more than write one of those Circulars that nobody ever reads anyhow?"

He grinned. "I'll have to toss a coin before I can answer that one. Much as I dislike Drongo Kane I'd hate to be on the same side as Billinghurst!"

3

When Grimes arrived at Port Last, on Ultimo, he was not in a good temper. The matter calling him away from Port Forlorn had been too urgent for him to wait for a regular sailing, so he had pressed the Deep Space tug *Rim Malemute* into service. She was an enormously powerful little brute, designed to go a long way in a short time. She was an assemblage of highly specialized machinery packed into a tin can, with no waste space whatsoever.

Williams, her skipper, brought her in as spectacularly as usual, applying the thrust of her inertial drive only when it seemed inevitable that the *Malemute* and her people would be smeared over the landing apron. Grimes, who was a guest in the control room, remarked coldly, "I almost lost my last meal. Not that it would have been much loss."

The tug skipper laughed cheerfully. He and Grimes were old friends and shipmates, and he had often served as the Commodore's second in command in *Faraway Quest*. He said, "You wanted to get here in a hurry, Skipper, and I got you here in a hurry. As for the tucker—this little bitch isn't an Alpha Class liner."

"Isn't she? You surprise me, Williams."

Grimes watched, through the viewport, the ground car that was coming out to the *Malemute*. Through the transparent canopy he could see two men. One was Giles, the Port Captain, the other was Dunbar, Rim Runners' Local Astronautical Superintendent. As the tug was in from another Rim Worlds port there were no Customs, Health, or Immigration officials. He said, "I'd better go to start sorting things out. I'll let you know where to send my baggage."

"Aren't you living aboard, Skipper?"

"If I'm a sardine in my next incarnation I'll think about it—but not until then."

Grimes went down to the airlock, the doors of which opened as he reached them, and walked down the ramp while it was still being extruded. As he was doing so the ground car came to a halt and Giles and Dunbar, both tall skinny men, got out. Giles was in uniform and saluted. Dunbar bowed stiffly. Grimes bowed in return.

"Glad to see you here, Commodore," said Dunbar.

"Thank you, Captain."

"Perhaps some refreshment before we get down to business. . . ."

"Thank you, but no. We adjusted our clocks to your local time for the last week of the voyage and I had breakfast before we landed." He looked at his watch. "0930 I make it."

"That is correct, sir."

Grimes got into the front of the car with Dunbar. Giles said that he was going aboard *Rim Malemute* to see Williams to handle the arrival formalities. Dunbar drove off, wasting no time.

Grimes looked with interest at the berthed ships as they passed them—*Rim Cougar*, *Rim Panther*, the Shakespearean Line's *Othello*, the Waverley Royal Mail's freighter *Countess of Ayrshire*. It could have been Port Forlorn, but for the weather. The sky overhead was blue, with a very few white clouds, not a dismal gray overcast—mainly natural, but contributed to by the smoke from the towering stacks of Lorn's heavy industry. Ahead, once they were through the main gates, was the city of Port Last, and beyond the white and red buildings towered the snowcapped pinnacles of the Ultimate Range. The road ran straight as an arrow through fields of wheat, some still green and some already golden. In these latter the harvesters, looking like huge mechanical insects, were busily working.

Ultimo, thought Grimes. *The Granary of the Rim Worlds. A planet of farmers. A world where anything, anything at all, is welcome as long as it breaks the deadly monotony. Like Elsinore, another farming world, but dairy products rather than grain, where compulsive gambling is the main social problem. . . .*

He asked Dunbar, "Where have they got young Pleshoff?"

"In the Central Jail, Commodore. I could have got him out on bail, but thought that if I did he'd be getting into more trouble."

"What are the charges, exactly?"

"As far as we're concerned, mutiny. As far as the civil authorities are concerned, drug addiction. I should have liked to have held Captain Gaynes and his Chief Officer as witnesses—but, as you know, *Rim Caribou* was already behind schedule and it would have taken too much time to get reliefs for them. But they left affidavits.''

"Mphm. What do you think, Captain?''

"What can I think? The young fool was in the control room, testing gear an hour before lift-off, while Gaynes was in my office and the Chief Officer was seeing the ship buttoned up for space. The engineers had been doing last minute maintenance on the inertial drive, had made a test run on one twentieth power and then, with departure time so close, had left it on Stand By. Pleshoff slammed it into maximum thrust and the old *Caribou* went up like a rocket. Gaynes and I saw it from my office window. It shook us, I can tell you. Then Pleshoff thought he'd try his hand at a few lateral maneuvers. He wiped the radio mast off the top of the spaceport control tower. He buzzed the market place in Port Last—and it was market day, too, just to improve matters. By this time the Chief and Second Officers had managed to break into the control room. They overpowered him and got the ship back into her berth—just as the entire police force came screaming in through the spaceport gates.''

"And what does he say?''

"That it seemed a good idea at the time.''

"Mphm. I suppose that all of us, as junior officers, have wanted to become instant captains. This drug addiction charge . . . do you think it will stick?''

"It'll stick all right. Pleshoff was running around

with a very unsavoury bunch of kids of his own age, bearded boys and shaven-headed girls. The Blossom People, they call themselves.''

"There are Blossom People on Francisco. I suppose they modeled themselves on these originals.''

"Probably. The gang that he was mixed up in seem to have a source of supply for—what do they call the muck?—dreamy weed. Ugh!''

"They smoke it?''

"Yes. In long, porcelain pipes. *They* claim that it's not habit forming. *They* claim that it's no worse than alcohol, that its effects are far less injurious. They even have a religion based on it.''

"Is this . . . this dreamy weed grown locally?''

Dunbar laughed. "On Ultimo? You must be joking, Commodore. Every square inch of soil on this planet has to nourish the sacred grain. It's smuggled in, from somewhere. The Police and the Customs are running around in small circles trying to get their paws onto the runners. But even the pushers are too smart for them.''

The car had entered the city now, was running through a wide street on either side of which were low, graceful stone houses. The houses gave way to shops, to office buildings, taller and taller as the vehicle approached the centre. And then they were in the great square, with the fountains and the statue of some Ancient Greek-looking lady proudly holding a sheaf of wheat. Surrounding the square were the official buildings—Town Hall, City Library, State Church, Aero-Space Authority, Police Headquarters, and Prison. The jail was a cylindrical tower, windowless except at ground level. It was well proportioned, graceful even—but it looked grim.

Dunbar said, "I've warned them that we're coming. They'll let us in."

"As long as they let us out," said Grimes.

4

The police lieutenant in charge of the ground floor office eyed Grimes and Dunbar as though they were candidates for admission. "Yes?" he barked.

"I am Captain Dunbar," said the Local Astronautical Superintendent. "This gentleman is Commodore Grimes."

The policeman's manner softened very slightly. He asked, "And what can I do for you gentlemen?"

"We wish to see Mr. Pleshoff. Colonel Warden said that it would be in order."

"Oh, yes. Pleshoff." The swarthy and burly young man leafed through a book on his desk. "We still have him."

Pleshoff, thought Grimes. *With no "Mister." But if you get on the wrong side of the law you soon lose your rank and status.*

"Cell 729," muttered the lieutenant. He raised an imperious hand and a constable obeyed the summons. "Bamberger, take these visitors to see the prisoner Pleshoff."

"It is a work period, sir."

"I know that. But I think that the sovereign state

of Ultimo can afford to dispense with his services for half an hour, or even longer.''

"Follow me, please, gentlemen,'' said the brawny Bamberger. He led the way to a bank of elevator doors. He addressed a grille set in the nearest one, said. "Constable Bamberger, No. 325252, with two visitors, Commodore Grimes and Captain Dunbar.'' Then, to his charges, "Stand beside me, please. One on either side of me.'' And again to the grille, "Constable Bamberger and party positioned.''

There was a flash of intense light, lasting for the briefest fraction of a second. Grimes allowed himself to wonder how he would look in the instantaneous photograph. The door slid open to reveal an empty cage. There was no control panel. The door silently shut as soon as they were all inside. Bamberger said, "Level 33.'' There was only the slightest tug of acceleration to indicate that they were being slowly carried upwards.

Grimes said, "I take it that your various robots are programmed to obey only the voices of prison staff.''

"I cannot answer that question, sir.''

"Mphm. And I suppose, too, that the elevators move very slowly unless some key word or phrase is used, so that any prisoner attempting to escape from an upper level in one cage would find that those on the ground floor had been given ample time to prepare for his reception.''

"I cannot answer that question, sir.''

"If the machinery running the elevators obeys

only the voices of the guards," said Dunbar, "how could a prisoner persuade it to work for him?"

"In the history of penology," said Grimes, "there are many instances of prisoners persuading guards to help them to escape. And not only with a knife or gun in the back."

"I'm afraid that I can't see Pleshoff doing any bribery," said Dunbar. "Not on Rim Runners' Third Officer's salary. I couldn't do it on mine."

"Mphm," grunted Grimes, and Bamberger looked relieved at the change of subject.

"What work do the prisoners do?" asked Grimes.

"Pleshoff, sir," said the constable, "is in the workroom where playmaster components are assembled. All the convicts receive full Award rates for whatever work they are doing. In the case of a prisoner not yet tried and convicted, even when undeniably guilty of the offense with which he is charged, he is allowed to keep the money he earns after the cost of his keep has been deducted. After conviction, of course, all his earnings revert to Consolidated Revenue."

"Mphm." Grimes turned to Dunbar. "I'm surprised that our Mr. Pleshoff hasn't been up before the Beak yet."

"He's had to take his place in the queue, Commodore."

"So they're keeping you busy," said Grimes to Bamberger.

The constable's wooden face at last betrayed some emotion. "It's these Blossom People, sir. They get a lungful of dreamy weed and the things they get up to aren't at all funny. We never have the same trouble with *proper* criminals."

"I suppose not. A proper criminal you just regard as one of the family."

Bamberger gave Grimes a very nasty look, then lapsed into sulky silence.

"But they are becoming a menace," said Dunbar. "The Blossom People, I mean."

"I suppose they are," said Grimes. Performing aerobatics in a 3,000 ton spaceship certainly could be classed as being a menace.

"Floor 33," announced Bamberger. He led the way out through the opening door.

Most of Floor 33 was occupied by the workroom. Through the space ran long, slow-moving conveyor belts. Industriously engaged at these were about a hundred men, each of whom was dressed in drab gray coveralls, each of whom had his number stenciled on to the chest and back of his garment. Blue-and-silver uniformed guards strolled watchfully along the lines, and other guards stood behind mounted guns of some kind in inward-facing balconies. *Those screwdrivers*, thought Grimes with a twinge of apprehension, *could be used as weapons. And the soldering irons. . . . But how long would a prisoner who tried to attack a guard last? Not long.* He transferred his attention to an almost completed playmaster that was sliding past him. He wondered if the machine in his own home had been assembled in a place like this.

One of the guards who had more silver braid on his sleeves than the others came to meet them. He said,

"Commodore Grimes? Captain Dunbar? You wish to see Pleshoff, Number 729. You may use the refreshment room. It will not be required for general use until the next smoke, forty five minutes from now. Take these gentlemen there, Bamberger."

"Yes, Sergeant."

The refreshment room was grim, gray, cheerless. It contained an ice-water dispenser and dispensers for tea and coffee. Bamberger asked if they wanted a drink. Dunbar refused one. The constable drew paper cups of coffee for Grimes and himself. The fluid was lukewarm, black, and bitter and could have been an infusion of anything at all but what it was called.

Escorted by two guards Pleshoff came in. Grimes remembered the young man, had interviewed him when he applied for a position in Rim Runners. He had been a junior officer in Trans-Galactic Clippers and had met a girl from Faraway when his ship had carried a number of Rim Worlds passengers on a cruise. He seemed to remember that Pleshoff had married the girl—yes, he had applied for an extension of leave during his honeymoon. And hadn't Pleshoff's captain mentioned to him, not so long ago, that the marriage had broken up?

There are some men who look like spacemen, like officers, no matter what they are wearing. Pleshoff was not one of them. Out of uniform—or in the wrong uniform—he looked like a very ordinary, very frightened young man. *At least he didn't look like a criminal*, thought Grimes.

The Commodore said to the guards, "Do you

think that you could leave us alone with the . . . er
. . . prisoner?''

Bamberger said, "These gentlemen were
vouched for by Colonel Warden."

One of the other men asked, "Aren't you Commodore Grimes, sir? *The* Commodore Grimes?''

"There's only one of me as far as I know," said
Grimes. "On *this* Continuum."

Bamberger was puzzled by this remark and said
doubtfully, "We have to ask the Sergeant."

But the Sergeant was agreeable, and after a few
minutes Grimes, Dunbar, and Pleshoff had the refreshment room to themselves, the two superinten-
dents seated on a hard wooden bench and the young
officer facing them, perched on a chair that looked
even harder than their own seat.

5

"And now, Mr. Pleshoff," said Grimes sternly, "what have you to say for yourself?"

"I suppose it's no good my saying that I'm sorry, sir."

"It's not," Grimes told him. *But,* he thought, *I'm sorry. I'm sorry to see a youngster ruin his career.*

"I suppose, sir, that I'm finished with Rim Runners."

"I'm afraid, Mr. Pleshoff, that you're finished in space. After what you did, your Certificate of Competency will have to be dealt with. There's no way out of it. But I don't think that we shall be pressing the mutiny charge."

"Thank you, sir."

"You haven't much to thank me for, Mr. Pleshoff. You're on the beach. You still have to face the drug charges. But I shall instruct our legal people to do what they can for you."

"Thank you, sir."

"And you might do something for me."

"Anything I can, sir." Pleshoff was pitifully eager.

"I'll be frank with you. Until now I've never taken this drug business seriously. I've thought, if people want to blow their minds, let 'em. It just never occurred to me that anybody in a position of trust, of responsibility, would get . . . hooked? Is that the right word?"

"But I'm not hooked, sir. I tried the dreamy weed only once, and they told me that its effects would be for that night only."

"And who," demanded Grimes sharply, "are *they?*"

Pleshoff's immature features set into a mask of stubbornness. He muttered, "Keep them out of it. They're my friends."

"You mean," said Grimes, "that *she's* your friend."

"Yes," admitted the young man. And then the words poured out. "I've been very lonely, sir. Ever since Sheila and I broke up. Then I met this girl, here, in Port Last. It was in the park. I'd been given the afternoon off and had gone for a walk. You know how it is, sir. You meet somebody and you sort of click. She's like the girls I used to know at home. You know—more free in her talk than the girls out here on the Rim Worlds, more way out in her dress. I took her to dinner that evening. She decided on the place. A little restaurant. Intimate. Candles on the tables, and all that. The menu on a blackboard. I didn't know until then that there were such places out here. That was just the first night, of course. There were other nights. We . . . we became friendly. And with the ship on a regular trade, coming in to

Port Last every three weeks or so, I . . ." he grinned weakly, "I had it made.

"She had other friends, of course. All in the same age group. One night she asked me round to a party at one of their places. There was music, of course, and plenty to drink, and things to nibble on, and we were all dancing some of the time, and talking some of the time. You know.

"And then the chap who was throwing the party got up and said, 'Quiet, everybody! Silence in Court! I have an announcement!' Then he went on to say that the pusher had come good at last, and that the gateway to never was open. This didn't make any sense to me. He started passing out long, pretty, porcelain pipes, and then brought out from somewhere a can of what looked like a greenish tobacco. 'What is it?' I asked my girl. 'Where were *you* dragged up?' she asked me. 'After all we mean to each other, don't tell me that you're a block.' "

"A block?" asked Grimes.

"It's what they call stiff and stodgy and conventional people, sir. Well, I told her that I wasn't a block. Then she said that I must be, otherwise I'd recognise dreamy weed when I saw it. Well, I'd heard about dreamy weed, of course, but you never see it in the Academy, although when I was there, for my pre-Space training, two senior cadets were booted out for smoking it. And there's something in TG Clippers' Company's Regulations about not being allowed aboard their ships. So I wasn't keen on trying it and said that we were lifting off the next day.

"She told me that I'd be right as rain in the morning. She told me, too, that to get the full benefit of it you had to smoke it with somebody, somebody towards whom you felt affectionate. If I wouldn't smoke with her, she was going to smoke with . . . the name doesn't matter.

"You know what it's like, sir. How a girl can make you do things you wouldn't do ordinarily."

" 'Lord,' "quoted Grimes, " 'the woman tempted me, and I fell.' "

"Who said that, sir?"

"A man called Adam. Rather before your time, and even mine. But go on."

"It was odd, sir. The smoke, I mean. She and I shared the pipe, passing it back and forth between us. It seemed that I was inhaling something of her, and that she was inhaling something of me. And it was like breathing in a fluid, a liquid, rather than a gas. A warm, sweet, very smooth liquid. And then, somehow, as we smoked we were . . . doing other things." Pleshoff blushed in embarrassment. "The people round us were . . . doing the same. But it wasn't always boys with girls. There were some boys with boys, and there were girls together. And the lights were dim, and dimmer all the time, and redder, and redder, like blood. But it wasn't frightening. It was all . . . warm, and . . . cosy. And there was a pulsing sound like a giant heartbeat. It must have been my own heart that I was hearing, or her heart, or the hearts of all of us. And we were very close, the two of us, all of us. And. . . .

"And we reached our climax. It's the usual way of

putting it, sir, and the words are the right words, but . . . can you imagine an orgasm that's an implosion rather than an explosion? And after that there was the slow, slow falling into a deep velvety darkness, a warm darkness. . . .

"And. . . .

"And then it was morning. Most of the others were waking up too. It should have all looked very sordid in the first light, naked bodies sprawled everywhere, but it didn't. And I felt fine, just fine, as fine as everybody looked, as fine as I knew that I looked myself. Somebody had made coffee, and I'd never tasted coffee as good before. It tasted the way that coffee smells when it's being ground. And my cigarette tasted the way that somebody else's cigar usually smells. I'd have liked to have stayed for breakfast with the others, but I had to be getting back to the ship. After all, it was sailing day. So I got back to the ship. I was still feeling fine—on top of the world, on top of all the worlds. I just breezed through all the things I had to do."

"Including testing the gear," remarked Grimes.

Pleshoff's face lost its animation. "Yes, sir. The gear. I was there, by myself, in the control room. I saw that the inertial drive was already on Stand By. And then, quite suddenly, the thought came to me, 'Why shouldn't I show the old bastard—sorry, sir, the Old Man I mean—that he's not the only one who can handle a ship?' I knew that he was still in Captain Dunbar's office, and I thought it'd be a fine joke if he saw his precious *Caribou* lifting off without him."

"Mphm. A very fine joke," commented Grimes.

"You may consider yourself highly fortunate that nobody was hurt or killed. Mphm. I suggest that you tell the authorities the name of your host on that unfortunate evening—although no doubt the local detective force is quite capable of finding it out for themselves. The real villain, of course, is the pusher. If you could name him you'd probably get off with a light sentence."

"I can't," said Pleshoff dully. "And if I could, I wouldn't."

Grimes shook his head sadly. "I don't know what trade you'll be entering after the authorities turn you loose—but whatever it is, you'll find that schoolboy code of honor a disadvantage." He got to his feet. "Well, Mr. Pleshoff, we'll do our best for you. We pride ourselves that we look after our own. But I'm afraid that you won't be one of our own for very much longer."

6

"I don't know what today's young people are coming to," complained Captain Dunbar as he and Grimes left the jail. "Drugs. Orgies."

"I've never taken part in an orgy," said Grimes rather wistfully. "Have you?"

"Of course not!" snapped Dunbar, looking at his superior in a rather dubious manner. Then, apparently having decided that the Commodore must have been joking, he went on, "Until now we've been clear of all this sort of thing on the Rim Worlds. I always said that it was a big mistake to open these planets to intergalactic trade."

"Mphm. Where am I staying, by the way?"

"We've booked you into the Rimrock House, Commodore."

Grimes sighed. There was a Rimrock House at Port Forlorn, on Lorn, another one at Port Farewell, on Faraway, yet another at Port Edgell, on Thule. From time to time he had stayed at them all. They were the most expensive hotels on the Rim Worlds—but by no means the best. He would have preferred some place with a less pretentious menu but far better food, with the staff not rigged out like Galactic High Admirals, but with far better service. But it would be only for a few days, until he had this *Rim Caribou* mess sorted out.

The Rimrock House was one of the huge buildings fronting on to the Central Square. Dunbar drove Grimes the short distance, although he would rather have walked, and promised that he would have the Commodore's gear picked up from *Rim Malemute* and sent out to the hotel.

Grimes left the car, walked over the sidewalk to the big doorway, through the force field that prevented the atmosphere of the hotel from being tainted by the excellent fresh air outside. On a world such as Lorn there would have been some point to it, but on Ultimo it was merely a very expensive absurdity. He nodded to the gorgeously uniformed doorman who had saluted him as though he were at least the Federation's First Space Lord. He went to the huge desk behind which a half dozen very pretty girls were chirping to each other like colorful inmates of an aviary. Eventually one of them condescended to notice him.

"Sir?"

"My name is Grimes. I am booked in here."

"Would that be Commodore Grimes, sir?" asked the tall blonde, statuesque in her form-revealing trouser suit of crimson dermitex.

"Yes."

"There is a Carlottigram for you, sir. It came in only a few minutes ago." She handed Grimes the dark blue envelope.

What now? he wondered as he ran a fingernail along the seal line. *What now?* The envelope tidily fell apart. He looked at the message it had contained.

From: Officer Commanding Rim Worlds Navy
To: Commodore   Grimes,   D.S.M.,   O.C.,
    F.H.S.C., R.W.N.R.
Copies: c/o Rimrock House, Port Last, Ultimo
        c/o Tug, Rim Malemute, at Port Last, Ul-
        timo
        c/o Dock Office, Rim Runners, Port Last,
        Ultimo
Text: As and from date of origination you are to
    consider yourself called to Active Service, Rim
    Worlds Navy, Pay and Allowances as for Com-
    modore First Class, Expenses as requisite. You
    are to cooperate with Police, Customs and other
    authorities in investigation of drug smuggling.
    Indefinite leave of absence from Rim Runners
    arranged, (Signed) Kravitz.

"Mphm," grunted Grimes thoughtfully. He could imagine what had been happening. High-up politicians must have been getting concerned about the general deterioration of Rim Worlds morals, and some of them must have demanded that the Navy do something about the smuggling in of drugs. And Admiral Kravitz—Grimes could just picture him—must have said, "We'll put Commodore Grimes on the job. Anything at all off-beat is right up his alley." And if Grimes were successful in stopping the traffic the Navy would take the credit. If he made a mess of things, it would be pointed out that, after all, he was only a Reserve Officer, not Navy proper. On past occasions Sonya had worked with him—but that had been when the Federation and the Confederacy had been acting in concert. On this occasion they would not be. The majority of Federated Planets approved the permissive society. The Rim Worlds did not, repeat not.

Oh, well, thought Grimes, *I suppose I'd better do something about something. For a start, I'd better organize transport for myself. Billy Williams is a Reserve Commander, and* Rim Malemute *is rated as a naval auxiliary vessel. And the Navy has a yard here, at Port Last, and an armory. It's time I did some telephoning. It's just as well that the Admiralty will be footing the bills.*

A smartly uniformed boy took him up to his suite. Once there Grimes called *Rim Malemute,* by now hooked into the planetary telephone service, and told Williams to come out to see him as soon as possible. Then he spoke to Rim Runners' Port Last Manager, telling him that he, Grimes, had been called to Active Service. He dictated a Priority Carlottigram to be sent to Admiral Kravitz, requesting the services of the *Malemute* and her personnel. He rang the O.I.C. Port Last Base, introducing himself and warning the officer that probably he would require some modifications made to the tug. He sent another Carlottigram, this one to Sonya, saying, *Involved in fun and games. See if you can get yourself asked to the party.* He caught Captain Dunbar at his office, and told him what was happening. Finally he rang the Port Last Chief Collector of Customs.

"Grimes here. Commodore Grimes. I've been

instructed to work with you people on this drug running business.''

"Oh, yes, Commodore. The Navy told us that they were putting a senior officer on to it. Hang on a moment, will you? There's a friend of yours here would like a word with you."

A friend? thought Grimes. *If I had any friends on this world they wouldn't be in the Customs Department.*

But he recognized the face that appeared in the little screen of the telephone. It was Billinghurst, who said, "A very good day to you, Commodore. I suppose you came here over the *Rim Caribou* affair. I was here when it happened. There's been a conference of all the senior Customs Officers of the Rim Worlds. Yes, about this drug business." He laughed fatly. "I think you'll admit, now, that sending out Circulars isn't quite good enough!"

7

In the days that followed Grimes was busy. The modifications to *Rim Malemute*—mainly the fitting of weaponry—he left in Williams' capable hands, concerning himself with setting up some kind of an organization and with reading all the official reports that were made available to him. Pleshoff, he learned, had been very unlucky. In the vast majority of cases those who smoked dreamy weed functioned normally on awakening. He learned, too, that the drug was not one on which one became hooked, although those who had participated in a dream time, as it was called, wished to repeat the experience as soon as possible. But, as far as he could determine, the stuff was no more dangerous than alcohol, and its over-all effects were far less damaging. Still, he had been ordered to help stamp out the traffic—and, as Sonya had said, there were far too many utterly unworthy people making far too big profits from it.

For much of the time he was having to work with Billinghurst who, even though Port Forlorn was his own bailiwick, had been put in general charge of the investigation by his Department. Grimes acquired a grudging respect for the man's capabilities although it was still impossible to like him. Billinghurst, however, insisted on treating Grimes as an old friend. His attitude was, we're both Lorners. We have to stand together against these Ultimo hicks.

He said, "We'll not be able to rely too much on the police, Commodore. They're like all policemen, everywhere. When it comes to dealing with members of the criminal classes they're quite efficient, but when they tangle with students, or spheres, they go all hysterical."

"Spheres?" asked Grimes.

"You should study the jargon. They call themselves spheres. They call people like us blocks. We block the spheres from rolling."

"And just how do the . . . er . . . spheres roll, Mr. Billinghurst?"

"Doing anything tonight, Commodore? There's a big roll around at the Dominey Hall. You and I will have to wear false beards and dress the part; spheres come in all ages and sizes. Young Pahvani—his sister is in your office—will be with us. He's been growing his own beard so he can play the part of a sphere if necessary. He'll tell you what to wear, and all the rest of it."

Grimes changed into his sphere outfit in Pahvani's room, in the unpretentious hotel in which the young Customs Officer was living. He surveyed himself rather dubiously in the full-length mirror. Black leather shorts—but that part of it wasn't so bad, he was used to wearing shorts with uniform. Bare legs—well, at least he maintained a good tan. Ornate, metal-studded sandals, looking like the sort of footwear that Roman legionaries must have worn. A short shirt, worn outside the shorts, basically dark green but liberally decorated with improbable scarlet and orange blossoms. A string of glass beads, each one a different shade of blue, and each one perfectly spherical. And the beard . . . it matched the hair of his head perfectly, but that was all that could be said in its favour. It was not the sort of beard that Grimes would ever have grown. It was too long, too untidy, untrimmed, uncombed.

There was one consolation; Billinghurst, who did not have the build for this sort of rig, looked even worse than Grimes, his spindly legs uglily incongruous under the gross bulk of his body. Sub-Inspector Pahvani looked quite good. His beard suited him. He could have been an old-time Indian mystic.

It was only a short walk from the hotel to the Dominey Hall, which was situated in the Old Town suburb of Port Last, differing from the ancient sheet metal buildings around it only in size. It was a huge barn of a place with no pretentions to architectural style. Projected into the air above it, in huge, shimmering letters of blue fire, were the words:

TONITE! TONITE!
ROLL-AROUND
TONITE!

Already there were crowds converging on the hall—men, of all ages, dressed as Grimes and his companions were dressed, girls and women, shaven-headed, most of them, similarly attired, although their shorts were much shorter and many of the shirts were practically transparent.

There were police, too, obvious in their blue and silver uniforms. One of them, when Grimes stopped to stare at the crowd, poked him quite painfully with his club, snarling, "Move along there, you bearded wonder! Move along!" Grimes decided to move along. Billinghurst chuckled and murmured, "You see what I mean about the Police Force, John."

"I see, Joe. And I feel it!"

They reached the door, where Pahvani paid the admission for all three of them. There were no seats in the hall. There was a platform in the centre of the floor, as yet unoccupied. The glaring lights overhead were red and green, blue and yellow. The air was hot and already heavy with the odour of perspiring and not overly clean humanity. Many of the women had already removed their shirts and a few of the men had done so.

"What band tonight, Francis?" asked Billinghurst casually.

"The Music of the Spheres, sir."

"Watch it!" snarled Billinghurst.

"The Music of the Spheres, Joe."

"Appropriate, I suppose," commented Grimes. He saw that a circle of flooring in the centre of the platform was sinking, was vanishing from sight. Some sort of elevator, he supposed. It would have been impossible for the bandsmen to struggle to their places through this crowd.

Yes, it was an elevator. It brought up the

instrumentalists—three bearded men with electric guitars, three more with small drums, one seated at a piano, and an enormously fat blonde girl who was holding a microphone.

They started almost at once—the guitars snarling, the drums thudding, the piano holding the tune together. The fat girl yelled into the microphone and her voice, vastly amplified, came at them from all corners of the hall.

"Driftin'
"An' dreamin',
"No lyin',
"No schemin',
"Just you, an' me,
"An' he, an' she,
"Just we,
"Ain't yer gonna drift an' dream some time with me?"

So it went on, for quite some time. Grimes was not enjoying himself much. He suspected that Billinghurst was not either. But young Pahvani was reveling in the music with its odd, broken rhythm—*like an inertial drive unit slightly on the blink,* thought Grimes nastily—as were most of the others in the crowd. But the real Roll-Around had not yet started.

When it did there was, at last, some rhythm in the music—unsubtle, compelling. As though stirred by a giant spoon the crowd began to move, clockwise, around the hall, marching in step to the insistent drums, stepping high, bringing feet thudding down on the reverberant floor. It was impossible not to join in, physically as well as psychologically. To the snarling guitars and growling drums they marched, to the amplified bass beat of the flogged piano, to the words that the fat woman was belting out in an almost baritone.

"Rolling free, rolling free!
"Give a shock to the blocks—One, two, three!
"Oh, we'll roll the bastards under
"And we'll break them all asunder,
"Rolling free, rolling free, rolling free!"

Grimes was singing as loudly as anybody. So was Pahvani. Billinghurst was merely muttering the words, without enthusiasm.

Round, and round, and round again. Pahvani had got his shirt off somehow. Grimes, sweating profusely, would have liked to have done the same, but in this crush it was impossible. He saw that some of the women had, with fantastic agility, contrived to strip themselves stark naked.

"Over land, over sea, we go rolling, rolling free,
"And we'll always go rolling along!
"Over hill, over dale, you will see our dusty trail,
"As we always go rolling along."

Round, and round, and round again. Tramp, stamp, tramp, *stamp!* Overhead the lights were swinging to the percussive beat of the music.

"An' all you blocks stop growlin',
"Or this is what we'll do!
"The spheres was made for rollin',
"They'll roll right over you!"

"I was hoping," gasped Billinghurst, contriving to whisper and pant simultaneously, "to pick something up here."

"That one looks quite nice," suggested Grimes, who had got his second wind. "A bit sweaty, but aren't we all?"

"No . . . not . . . *that!* Information."

"A rolling sphere gathers no moss," Grimes told him.

Round, and round, and round again. Tramp, tramp, tramp! Stamp, stamp, *stamp!*

"When the spheres come rolling in,
"When the spheres come rolling in,
"We're gonna be in that number
"When the spheres come rolling in!"

To Grimes' right there was a skinny, half naked, almost breastless girl who had been edging closer and closer to him with every circuit of the floor. He was beginning to wonder if a pick-up were intended, was trying to work out ways and means of achieving a painless brush-off. She just wasn't his type. And then he saw that a plump, copiously perspiring young man had joined her in this dance that was more like a march. He heard him whisper to her, "0200 hours at the Fitzroy Crossing. Pass it on!" His message delivered, he vanished into the mass of dancers.

Somehow the skinny girl had inserted herself between Grimes and the almost exhausted Billinghurst. She was singing softly, in time to the music,

"When the weed comes dropping in,
"When the weed comes dropping in,
"Oh two hundred, Fitzroy Crossing,
"When the weed comes dropping in!"

The music changed, but she went on singing,

"Dreamy free, dreamy free,
"Dreamy weed, dreamy weed, dreamy free
. . ."

She made a face at Billinghurst, flashed a smile at Grimes, and wriggled away through the crowd.

Round, and round, and round—but with every circuit edging closer to the exit.

"Oh, we'll roll, away up yonder!
"Oh, we'll roll, away up yonder!
"Oh, we'll roll, away up yonder!
"When they roll away up yonder we'll be there!"

And Billinghurst, getting his wind back, sang the final "We'll be there!" with great emphasis.

8

But they almost weren't there.

There was a minor riot outside the Dominey Hall. Accounts as to its cause differed. One morning paper said that a crowd, singing, "We'll roll the bastards under!" had charged a group of policemen. The other paper said that the police had charged a small group of people from the Roll-Around who were going their ways quite peacefully.

Actually it had been Grimes' fault. Those noisy songs, with their primitive rhythm, had carried him back in time, to when he was a young and normally rowdy cadet in the Federation's Survey Service. He had remembered something that he and his ship-mates had been fond of singing whenever there was a minion of the law within earshot. He had insisted on teaching the words to Billinghurst—who was not amused—to Pahvani—who was—and to a half dozen young men and girls who were going the same way as themselves.

"There's a policeman on his beat,
"Over there, over there!
"There's a policeman on his beat,
"Over there!

227

"There's a policeman on his beat,
"I can smell his sweaty feet,
"There's a policeman on his beat
"Over there!"

During the third, noisy rendition of this ditty a dozen policemen tried to silence the songsters. Punches were thrown. Stunguns were used, set so as to inflict the maximum pain without causing unconsciousness. A large body of revelers rushed to the aid of Grimes and his companions. Police air cars clattered overhead, dropping arrest-meshes, wire nets that ignored the specially treated police uniforms but that clung to everything else in a tight grip. The air cars ranged over the street like seine net fishermen over a school of fish. Their catch, dangling under the aircraft, was hauled ignominiously to the station house. Grimes, Billinghurst, and Pahvani would have spent the night in cells had not Pahvani, who had been acting as liaison officer between Police and Customs, been recognized by the lieutenant in charge. He had the three Lorners hustled away from the other prisoners, ostensibly for interrogation. Shouts of sympathy and encouragement followed them.

As soon as he could safely do so Billinghurst snarled, "You almost ruined everything, Commodore!"

"When among spheres—roll!" replied the unrepentant Grimes.

"You, Lieutenant whatever-your-name-is," snapped Billinghurst to the police officer. "I am the Chief Collector of Customs for Port Forlorn, in over-all charge of this drug investigation. This is

Commodore Grimes, of the Rim Worlds Navy, who's working with me." He glared at the Commodore. "Or against me, to judge by tonight's little effort. Sub-Inspector Pahvani you already know."

"And what can I do for you, sir?"

"I want vehicles, and I want men. Armed men."

"And a map," contributed Grimes. "And all the geographical information you can give us." He waited for Billinghurst to say something, then added, "It seems that there's to be a drop at Fitzroy Crossing. At 0200 hours tomorrow."

"There's a wall map in the Captain's office," said the lieutenant. "Follow me, please."

The map was a large scale topographical one, covering Port Last and the surrounding countryside to a distance of 50 kilometres from the City Centre. "The Fitzroy Crossing is not far from here," said the police officer, jabbing with his finger. "There's a bridge, as you see, both road and monorail. On the north side of the bridge there's Davidsham village—with one Senior Constable who, by this time, will be tucked up warm and snug in his little bed." He laughed. "I was stationed there myself before I was promoted to Sergeant. Nothing ever happens in Davidsham. Even so, I should hardly think that the drop will be to the north of the Crossing.

"Now, on the south side we have the wheatfields. And," his finger jabbed again, "*here* we have the racecourse. I hope you gentlemen can manage to be here for the Ultimo Cup Week—it's really something."

"Landing facilities?" asked Grimes, who was not at all interested in horses.

"You could set a cruiser down there, Commodore. And a couple of destroyers. No G.C.A. of course. Ha, ha."

"There probably will be," said Grimes. "A small beacon, mounted on a car. Mphm. Now, Mr. Billinghurst, if we go charging out there in police vehicles we'll scare off the reception committee—and whoever's making the delivery. I suggest that we land somewhere to the north of the racecourse, well away from the road, and make our way to the landing site on foot. We shall want a guide. Do any of your men know the district, Lieutenant?"

"I do, sir."

"Good. And have you any quiet cars? Inertial drive kicks up one helluva racket, especially on a still night like this."

"We have the blimps, sir. They have been developed especially for police use on this planet."

"They should do." And Grimes thought, *Once again the airship comes back into service*. He said, "But I thought you had no really serious crime on Ultimo."

"There are gambling schools, sir, very often meeting out in the country. They play a game of chance, tossing two coins. When it comes to catching the gamblers redhanded we find the silent approach technique very useful. The blimps are propeller driven, with almost noiseless electric motors."

"Make it blimps, then."

"Very good, sir. And now, if you'll excuse me,

I'll ring the Precinct Captain and start getting things organized.''

"Before you do, Lieutenant, is there a washroom handy? I'd like to get this artificial foliage off my face. I'd just hate to get it wound round a blimp's propeller.''

9

Airships had always fascinated Grimes. Now and again, on worlds lagging in technological development, and on planets whose people had a common-sense attitude towards unnecessary power consumption, he had been a passenger in such craft. The Shaara, for example, could build spaceships at least as good as anything built by Man, but for atmospheric flights they favored lighter-than-air machines.

The blimps of the Ultimo Police were well conceived, well designed, well constructed. They were semirigid ships rather than true blimps, however. They had heating coils inside their balloons to give the helium additional lift, and there was an arrangement of bands and nets whereby the lift could be reduced by compression of the gas. Water ballast was carried, but except in emergencies there would be no need for any valving of helium or dumping of ballast. Below the rigid spines were slung the gondolas, one to each ship, and each with a single pusher screw.

Grimes, Billinghurst, and Pahvani rode in the

leading ship, the one piloted by the police lieutenant. With them were four constables. Grimes sat with the pilot in the little control cab at the fore end of the gondola, watching everything with interest. Mooring lines were cast off by the ground crew, but the ship still sat stolidly on its skids, although above the gondola the gas bags, enclosed in their sausage-shaped integument, were swaying and creaking. The lieutenant's hand went to a switch on the control panel and almost immediately there was the subdued hum of an electric motor. *Decompression?* wondered Grimes. But apart from the mechanical noise, which soon stopped, nothing at all seemed to be happening.

The lieutenant swore under his breath. Then he called back into the main cabin, "Excuse me, Mr. Billinghurst, how much do you weigh?"

"I . . . I haven't checked lately, Lieutenant."

"Then it's time you did!" muttered the young man.

There was a fresh sound, the splashing of water on to the concrete of the blimpyard. Now the ship was rising, smoothly, silently, up past the lighted windows of the police barracks, up, up, until a checkered pattern of crisscrossing street lights, Port Last lay below her. Grimes poked his head out of an open side window, looked astern. One by one, great dark shapes, their black bulks in silhouette against the glow of the city lights, the other five airships were swimming upwards.

The lieutenant started his motor then. It was almost silent, and only a faint swishing sound came

233

from the propeller. Slowly he brought the ship round to her heading, explaining, "We have to be careful how we handle these things. They're just a little flimsy." Gradually the lights of the city, of the scattered outer suburbs, drifted astern.

It was a fine night, clear, almost windless. The single moon of Ultimo, named Ceres, was hanging high in the black sky, the empty sky of the Rim Worlds. It was just past its full but did not give much light; satellites so large as to be almost sister planets are rare throughout the Galaxy. Nonetheless, the surface of the Fitzroy River reflected what little illumination there was, a faintly gleaming silver ribbon winding through formless masses of darkness. On the horizon was the dim cluster of yellow lights that was Davidsham.

Silently the squadron flew on, invisible from the ground now that it was clear of the glare from the city, keeping the river to starboard, the distant village fine on the starboard bow. Grimes borrowed the pilot's night glasses. He could see, now, the straight black line that cut the silver ribbon. The bridge. . . . He looked more to his left, trying to pick out the racecourse, but without success.

"You'll not find it, sir," laughed the Lieutenant, "unless you've eyes like a cat. But you see the horseshoe bend, just this side of the village?"

"Mphm. Yes."

"There's a field there that's been harvested. That's where we're landing."

"And then we get out and walk."

"Yes. Then we get out and walk."

The airship was losing altitude as the pilot applied negative dynamic lift. Grimes could make out features on the ground below now, as long as they were not too far distant. He could see the paleness of the fields that were yet to be harvested, the darkness of those where reaping had already taken place. Another electric motor started up, and from above came a faint creaking as the gas bags were compressed. The ground seemed very close now, and seemed to be rushing past at a fantastic speed. Grimes started to worry about tall trees and the like, but told himself that the lieuteanant knew what he was doing. In any case, it would be unlikely that there would be any trees in the wheatlands to rob the precious grain of its nutriment.

The pilot snapped rapid orders to the other ships on his radio, then stopped the main motor, restarting it almost at once in reverse. The ground below slowly lost its retrograde progression relative to the ship, but was coming up to meet her as the buoyancy was squeezed out of her balloons. There was a dry crackling from under the gondola as the skids brushed the stubble. Then, with all motors stopped, she landed. Men jumped from the side doors, quickly and efficiently moored her with screw pegs.

"All ashore!" ordered the lieutenant cheerfully.

Grimes jumped down from the gondola to the ground, cursing to himself as the stubble scratched his bare calves and shins. He should have changed out of this absurd rig; getting rid of that insanitary beard had been a step in the right direction, but not far enough. It was fortunate that the correct footwear for a Roll-Around consisted of very heavy sandals. He was joined by Billinghurst and Pahvani. He stood with them to watch the other airships coming in. He wondered how those landing managed to avoid those already down, and was told by the Lieutenant that on occasions such as this dim lights were shown on the tops of the gas bags.

There was a very cautious flashing of down-pointed, shielded torches. The lieutenant detailed a man to stay with each ship, then said to Grimes, "You and the other two had better stay close to me, Commodore. We'll walk to the racecourse from here, making as little noise as possible. Before we get there we'll spread out to surround the position—just in case there's anybody there. If there's not—some of us will wait in the Owners' Stand, some by the Saddling Paddock and the rest by the Tote. That'll give us a good coverage."

"And good odds?" asked Grimes.

He did not much enjoy the walk over the fields. There was enough moonlight to make the going not too difficult, but the sharp spiny stubble was drawing blood with almost every step. And the air, despite the lack of wind, was decidedly chilly. And *things* were rustling in the dry stalks. He had visions of venomous reptiles, insects or the like, and was only slightly reassured when his guide whispered to him that it was only cats—of Terran origin—hunting a small and harmless (apart from its appetite for grain) indigenous rodent.

Behind him, despite his bulk, Billinghurst was moving silently, as was Pahvani, and as far as noise was concerned the policemen might not have been there at all. Grimes murmured something complimentary to the Lieutenant and was told that this was the Gaming Squad, used to creeping up on parties of gamblers. He asked if the fines collected from such desperate criminals sufficed to pay for the airships and other equipment, and was answered by a pained silence.

Whispered orders were passed back and the policemen spread out to surround the racecourse. Grimes could just hear the faint voices from the Lieutenant's wrist radio as the members of his force reached their assigned positions. Then the order was given to advance, with caution. Ahead, rails glimmered whitely in the faint moonlight. Grimes, following the leader, ducked under them and on to the track. There were vague shapes in front of them, moving towards them—but it was only the men who had entered the course by the Owners' Stand and who were now on their way to the Tote. They reported briefly to their officer that they had seen nobody, and that nothing larger than a cat had registered on their biodetectors.

Grimes looked at his watch. An hour to wait. Probably the receivers would not be here until just before the drop was due—assuming, of course, that this was the drop site.

He had hoped that the benches in the stand would be padded.

They were—but the padding had long since lost any softness it had ever possessed.

10

It was a long wait, in the cold and the dark, while the little moon, now past the meridian, slowly slipped down the starless sky. The policemen—and, to an only slightly lesser degree, Billinghurst and Pahvani—were used to vigils beside yet-to-be-sprung traps; Grimes was not. He wanted to be *doing* something. Finding that the lieutenant had a pass key that fitted the lock of the toilets under the stand he borrowed it, although what he really wanted was a smoke. His battered, stinking pipe was very comforting after he got it going and he was in no hurry to rejoin his comrades. Then, looking at his watch, he decided that he had better. The time was 0155 hours.

As soon as he was back outside he heard the noise. Something was approaching from the direction of the city, something in the sky. The irregular stuttering of a small inertial drive unit was unmistakable. He looked up, in the direction from which the sound was coming, but saw nothing. But it was not likely that the smugglers' aircraft would be showing running lights.

It was visible at last, but only when it dropped to a

landing in the centre of the ellipsoid formed by the track. It just sat there, but nobody came out of it. Its crew was waiting, just as the police were waiting.

Grimes looked at his watch again. 0201 . . . 0202. . . .

"Here it comes!" whispered the lieutenant.

Here it came.

At first it was no more than a barely audible, irritable muttering drifting down from the zenith. It became louder, but not much louder. The machine that finally dropped into sight was no more than a toy, no more than a model of a ship's boat. It might have accommodated the infant child of midget parents who had bred true, but nobody larger. But it could carry quite a few kilos of dreamy weed.

The police had their stunguns ready, trained on the smugglers' aircraft and on the robot, which were covered from three points—from the Owners' Stand, from the Saddling Paddock, from the Totalizator. The lieutenant had stationed his men well; whoever had come to pick up the consignment would be inside the effective range of the weapons, but each police party would be just outside the range of the guns of the others.

Somebody was coming out of the aircraft at last, walking slowly and cautiously towards the grounded robot spaceboat, hunkering down on the grass beside the thing.

"Fire," said the lieutenant in a conversational tone of voice, speaking into his wrist transceiver.

The air was alive with the vicious buzzing of the stunguns. The smuggler was frozen in his squatting posture, paralyzed, unable to stir so much as a finger. But the robot moved. Its drive unit hammered shockingly and unrhythmically and it shot straight upwards. Beams from hastily switched on police searchlights swept the sky like the antennae of disturbed insects—then caught it, held it, a tiny bright star in a firmament that had never known any stars. At least four machine rifles were hammering, and an incandescent tracer arched upwards with deceptive slowness. The lieutenant had drawn his laser pistol and the purple beam slashed across the darkness, power wasting and desperate. Some hapless night-flying creature caught by the sword of lethal light exploded smokily.

It might have been the machine rifles that found their mark, it might have been the laser pistol. Nobody ever knew. But the broken beat of the inertial drive ceased abruptly and the robot was falling, faster and faster, still held in the searchlight beams. It hit the ground almost exactly at the point of its initial landing.

It hit the ground—and, "Down!" shouted somebody. "Get down!"

It hit the ground, and where it struck an instantaneous flower of intolerable flame burgeoned, followed by a *crack!* that sounded as though the very planet were being split in two. The blast hit the grandstand, which went over like a capsizing windjammer—but, freakishly, the structure remained intact. Had it not done so there would have been serious injuries, at least to those upon it. Dazed, deafened, Grimes struggled to his feet, crept cautiously along the back of the bench upon which he had been sitting. Lights were flashing as men helped each other from the wreckage.

Billinghurst got clear of the stand before Grimes. He had found a torch and was running clumsily across the grass to the still smoking crater. The Commodore followed him. He gagged as the Customs Officer's light fell on the tangle of broken limbs and spilled entrails that had been the smuggler who had come out from the air car. The head was missing. After a cursory glance Billinghurst ignored the dead man, carried on to the wrecked vehicle, which had been blown on to its side. He shone his light in through the open door. The girl inside appeared to be uninjured, but she was very still. A strand of hair glowed greenly across her white face. Her hair? Grimes could see the beam of the torch reflected from her shaven, polished scalp. The fat man stooped, lifted the hank of green fibre, twisted it between his thick fingers, sniffed it.

"Dreamy weed," he said flatly. Then, "The poor little bitch got what she came for. It's the very last thing that she did get." He shifted the beam of his torch and Grimes saw that the girl's body, below the waist, was no more than a crimson pulp.

The Commodore looked away hastily, up to the empty blackness of the sky. Somewhere up there was a ship. Somewhere up there was somebody who had killed, ruthlessly, to destroy all evidence that could be used to stop his profitable racket.

"Losing your neutrality, Commodore Grimes?" asked Billinghurst.

11

Peter Fellini, Student.
Aged 19.75 Years, Local, 18.25 Years, Standard.
Inga Telfer, Artist.
Aged 25.50 Years, Local, 23.05 Years, Standard.

The identification of the bodies had presented no problems. Ultimo is one of those worlds where everybody is fingerprinted, where a record is made of everybody's retinal patterns and where coded information, including allergies and blood group, is tattooed in everybody's armpits.

The two victims were known to have been Blossom People. Fellini had been brilliant in his studies. Inga Telfer's swirling abstracts had been in great demand and had fetched good prices. Their deaths had been remarkably pointless; they had suffered the misfortune of being at the wrong place at the wrong time.

The identification of the ship that had made the drop was also easy. Immediately on return to Port Last Grimes and Billinghurst had gone to Aerospace

Control. The Duty Officer had at first been uncooperative—as far as he was concerned here were two spheres, albeit beardless ones, invading his office. But once credentials were produced he was very helpful.

Yes, the Tanagerine tramp *Ditmar* was at present in orbit about Ultimo, having signalled her intention of landing at first light. Her Master, one Captain Reneck, did not like pilotage in the dark. He had brought his ship into Port Last on quite a few occasions, but always during daylight hours. Yes, *Ditmar* was on a regular run between Ultimo and Eblis. She was chartered to bring shipments of minerals from the so-called Hell Planet, and to carry assorted foodstuffs back to the holiday resort in Inferno Valley. And where was she relative to Port Last, to the Fitzroy Crossing, shortly after 0200 hours? To judge by the elements of her orbit, constantly checked by ground radar, she must have been on the other side of the planet.

"Mphm," grunted Grimes doubtfully on learning this. At the time of the attempted escape of the robot, at the time of its destruction, line of sight communication between it and the mother ship would have been impossible. But there was no reason why *Ditmar* should not have left at least one relay station in orbit. If this were so, then she ran to a line of highly sophisticated electronic gadgetry not usually, if ever, found aboard a merchant vessel, a tramp freighter at that.

And Tanager. . . .

It was one of the older colonies, having been

settled during the Second Expansion. It was a Federated Planet, but rather peculiarly situated, being the only world with a human population in a sector of space that had been colonised by the Shaara. There was a Federation Survey Service Base on Tanager, a base that could be of vital strategic importance should Man and Shaara ever fall out again. The Tanagerines knew this, and every now and again talked of the economic advantages that would accrue if their world became part of the Shaara Empire—so the Federation went to great pains to try to keep them happy. And for many years now the foreign policy of the Rim Worlds Confederacy had been geared to that of the Interstellar Federation.

Don't let's be nasty to the Tanagerines, thought Grimes. But if *Ditmar's* Master had broken Rim Worlds laws he must expect some nastiness.

Grimes and Billinghurst were out at the spaceport at dawn to see *Ditmar* come in. The battered tramp dropped down carefully, with a caution that would not have been amiss in a vessel ten times her size. Although she was from one of the other Rim Worlds she was a foreign ship, so officials from Port Health, Immigration, and Customs were waiting for her. The Customs Officers were, in fact, out in force.

Ditmar bumbled in hesitantly, at last hovering a few feet over the beacons that marked her berth. Her inertial drive unit was a particularly noisy one. When at last it was stopped the short-lived silence was deafening—and broken by the tinny crash as the ship's tripedal landing gear hit the concrete. There was a long delay, and then the after-airlock door opened slowly and the ramp extruded. Billinghurst pushed himself to the head of the group of waiting officials, tramped heavily aboard. Grimes followed him.

Ditmar's Mate, a burly, swarthy young man in shabby uniform, received them. He mumbled, "You'll find all the papers in the Purser's Office, as usual."

"Take us to the Captain," snapped Billinghurst.

"This . . . This isn't usual."

"I know it's not usual." Billinghurst turned to give orders to his officers. "Spread out through the ship. Living quarters, control room, engine-room, everywhere."

"But, look, Mister. We're in from Eblis. *Eblis.* That's one of *your* bloody Rim Worlds, isn't it?"

"Take us to the Captain," repeated Billinghurst.

"Oh, all right, all right. You'll have to use the stairway, though, the elevator's on the blink."

Grimes and Billinghurst followed the officer up the internal spiral staircase. It didn't worry Grimes much, but by the time they got up to the Captain's flat the fat man was soaked with sweat, his face purple. The Mate knocked at the open door, said, "Two Customs Officers to see you, sir." Grimes glared at him. Admittedly his uniform, which he had put on for the occasion, was similar to Billinghurst's, but if this young oaf could not distinguish between different cap badges it was time that he started to learn.

"Come in, come in." Captain Reneck looked up

from his desk. "The cargo manifest and the store sheets are in the Purser's office. I don't have them here."

"I am the Chief Collector of Customs at Port Forlorn," began Billinghurst.

"Haven't you got your ports mixed?"

"And I am in over-all charge of an investigation. This gentleman with me is Commodore Grimes, of the Rim Worlds Navy."

"Indeed?" Captain Reneck's busy black eyebrows, the only noticeable feature of his pale, smooth face, lifted. "Indeed? A Customs Officer *and* a Commodore of the Rim Worlds Navy. Please be seated, gentlemen."

"Captain Reneck," said Billinghurst, "I'll waste no words. At approximately 0200 hours this morning, Port Last time, a powered container of dreamy weed—a powered, booby-trapped container of dreamy weed—made a landing at the Fitzroy Crossing."

"So? But at 0200 hours this morning I was not over Port Last, or the Fitzroy Crossing."

"Does your ship carry probes?" demanded Grimes. "Robot probes, remote-controlled? Is she fitted with the equipment to launch and guide and recover such probes?"

Reneck grinned. His ugly teeth showed yellow in his white face. "As a matter of fact she does, and she is. Tanager is a poor world and cannot afford specialized survey craft. All of our merchant ships—all of them tramps like this vessel—are so fitted as to be able to carry out survey work if required."

"Two people were killed this morning," said Billinghurst. "A young man and a young woman."

"I am very sorry to hear that," said Reneck, neither looking nor sounding sorry.

"What do you know about the container of dreamy weed that was dropped?" blustered Billinghurst.

"What should I know?"

"It must have come from your ship," said Grimes.

"How could it have done so? I was nowhere near the scene of the alleged smuggling."

"And murder."

"Murder, Commodore? Strong words. How could I, a law-abiding shipmaster, be implicated in murder? A naval officer like yourself, maybe, but not a merchant spaceman." He sighed. "Murder. . . ."

"Who's paying you?" snapped Billinghurst suddenly.

"The TSSL, of course. The Tanager State Shipping Line." He grinned with another display of discolored teeth. "Between ourselves, gentlemen, they could pay much better than they do."

"So something a little extra, over and above your salary, tax free," suggested Grimes.

"Really, Commodore . . . you wouldn't suggest that, surely."

"How many robot probes do you carry?"

"Three. You will find that number shewn on my store sheets, and you will find that number in the launching bay."

Billinghurst lumbered to his feet. "Let's get out of

here, Commodore Grimes.'' He turned to Reneck. ''My men are taking the ship apart. If they find so much as one strand of dreamy weed, may all the Odd Gods of the Galaxy help you. Nobody else will.''

12

The Odd Gods of the Galaxy did not have their peace disturbed. *Ditmar* was a clean ship—clean, that is, from a Custom Officer's viewpoint, although not necessarily from that of a spaceman. She was far scruffier than the generality of tramps. Painted surfaces were not only crying out for a fresh coat of paint but for the washing of what had been applied some time in the distant past. The ghosts of every meal that had been cooked in her galley since her maiden voyage still haunted her accommodation; the dirt of unnumbered worlds was trodden into her deck coverings.

But she was *clean*. There was not even any pornography in her officers' cabins. Nobody had a drop of liquor or a fraction of an ounce of tobacco over and above the permitted duty-free allowance. Her papers were in impeccable order. She was so clean, in fact, as to invite suspicion.

From the viewpoint of the authorities it was unfortunate that she was of Tanagerine registry. Had she been under any other flag it would have been possible to clap some of her personnel into jail on some trumped-up charge or another. A fight in a bar, started by a provocateur. . . . The imprisonment of all participants and, if necessary, innocent bystanders. The administration of "blabberjuice" in food or water. . . . Oh, it *could* have been done, but little, otherwise unimportant Tanager was a pet of the United Planets Organization. Billinghurst and the Port Last Chief of Police would have liked to have done it regardless, but orders were given to them to handle *Ditmar* with kid gloves before they could give orders of their own to their under cover agents.

Bugs, of course, were planted in the places of entertainment and refreshment frequented by *Ditmar's* crew. They picked up nothing of interest. The Tanagerines seemed to be enthusiastic amateur meteorologists to a man and discussed practically nothing except the weather. Bugs were planted aboard the ship herself—a Customs Searcher, of course, knows all the good hiding places aboard a vessel. The only sound that they recorded was a continuous, monotonous *whirrup, whirrup, whirrup*.

All that could be done was to delay the ship's departure on her return voyage to Eblis. At Grimes's suggestion the Port Last Department of Navigation Surveyor checked up on *Ditmar's* lifesaving equipment. One of her lifeboats was not airtight, and was condemned, and the stores in one of the others were long overdue for renewal. The faulty boat could have been repaired, of course, but the Surveyor's word was law. And, oddly enough, lifeboat stores were practically unprocurable at Port Last and would have to be shipped from Port Forlorn. So it went on. The

Master of a merchant vessel is peculiarly helpless when the Authorities of any port take a dislike to him.

Meanwhile, *Rim Malemute*, her armament fitted, was almost ready for space. Grimes was taking her to Eblis. Officially he was visiting that world to inspect port facilities, as the Rim Worlds Navy was thinking of opening a base there. Billinghurst wanted to come with him, saying that he wished to make arrangements for the setting up of a Customs Office at Inferno Valley. Grimes told him that this would look too suspicious, both of them leaving Port Last in the same ship. This was true, of course, but the real reason for the Commodore's refusal to cooperate was that he did not wish to share the cramped quarters aboard the little *Malemute* with a man of Billinghurst's bulk. Alternative transport was available, although not at once. TG Clippers' cruise liner, *Macedon*, was due shortly at Port Last, and Inferno Valley was her next port of call.

"Eblis," said Billy Williams, when he and Grimes were discussing matters prior to departure. "I've never been there, Skipper. What's it like?"

"Its name suits it, Commander Williams, very well indeed. It's mainly red desert, with rocks eroded by wind and sand into all sorts of fantastic shapes. It has volcanoes—big ones and little ones— like other worlds have trees. The atmosphere is practically straight sulphur dioxide. The inhabitants look like the demons of Terran mythology—horns and tails and all—but they're quite harmless, actually. Earth tremors are more common than showers of rain on normal worlds. The odd part about it is that as long as you keep away from the really dangerous areas you're as safe there as you are anywhere in the Galaxy. The planet is like a huge amusement park with all sorts of hair-raising rides; you get the illusion of risk with no real risk at all. That's why it's such a popular holiday resort."

"Inferno Valley . . . isn't that owned by a retired space captain?"

"Yes. Captain Clavering. He came out to the Rim quite some years ago, Owner/Master of a ship called *Sally Ann*. She was—of all things!—an obsolescent Beta Class liner. Far too big and expensive in upkeep for a little, one ship company. He'd been getting by somehow, just making ends meet, but when I met him he'd come to the end of the line. I was able to put a charter in his way; the Rim Worlds Universities were sending a scientific expedition to Eblis and we, Rim Runners, hadn't any ships either handy or suitable.

"So he went to Eblis. He and his wife, he told me later, quite fell in love with the valley in which the expedition set up its main camp. There are these quite fertile valleys all over the planet, actually, not too hot and the air quite breathable if you don't mind the occasional whiff of brimstone. But what gave him the idea of a holiday resort was a remark that he'd heard somebody—it may have been me—make: 'Anybody who comes out to the Rim to earn a living would go to hell for a pastime!'

"That was his start. He had people living in tents at first, with quite primitive facilities. He used his own *Sally Ann* to carry holidaymakers from the Rim

Worlds to this amusement park inferno. Then TG Clippers, when they started cruising, got into the act. Then the Waverley Royal Mail. Even the Dog Star Line. And Clavering never looked back.

"His old *Sally Ann* is still there, I believe. He doesn't use her himself—he's too busy being a resort manager. And I don't think he's sufficiently sentimental to hang on to her for old times' sake—it's just that the market for secondhand ships of that size is a very limited one."

Grimes carefully filled and lit his pipe. When it was going he said, "I rather like Clavering, and I'm pleased that he's done so well. I only hope that he's not mixed up in this dreamy weed business."

"I don't see why he should be, Skipper. He must be coining money in his legitimate business."

"Nobody is so rich that he can't use a few extra credits—especially when they're tax free. Too, very few people from the Inner Worlds would consider the possession, use, or even peddling of a drug like dreamy weed a crime. I'm not at all sure that I do myself. It's when the racketeers get mixed up in the trade that it's bad. It's when two young people get blown into messy tatters by the bastards they're working for."

"And it's when people make a religion out of what is, after all, just a pleasure," said Williams, who had his puritanical moments.

"If all religions had been like that," Grimes told him, "they'd have done far less harm over the ages."

Williams was not convinced.

13

Williams piled on the lumes all the way from Ultimo to Eblis. Grimes was in a hurry; he wanted to get there before Reneck's principal was fully advised as to what had been happening at Port Last. *Ditmar*, of course, could not legally use her Deep Space radio while in port, so any Carlottigrams originated by her Master would have to be handled by the Port Last G.P.O. And the Port Last post office telegraphists were on strike. Grimes did not know how much Billinghurst had to do with this, but suspected that it was plenty. The cause of the stoppage had been the quite justifiable dismissal of a shop steward for insolence. Who was Billinghurst's under cover man—the shop steward or the overseer who had fired him? Perhaps they were both Customs agents. Perhaps—but this was unlikely—the strike was coincidental.

The more Grimes thought about it the more sure he became that Eblis was the source of dreamy weed shipments to the other Rim Worlds. Inferno Valley was not a Rim Worlds Port of Entry, therefore there was no Customs Office on Eblis. In theory any ship bound for Eblis was supposed first to land on one of the worlds from which she could be entered inwards. *Ditmar*, for example, when she had first come out to the Rim had arrived at Port Edgell, on Thule, with a cargo of cheese from Elsinore. She had then loaded general cargo for Inferno Valley, and thereafter had shuttled between Eblis and the other Rim Worlds, mainly Ultimo, with regularity. As a foreign ship she had been liable to Customs inspection every time in, but as she was not from a foreign port the inspection, until this last time, had been a mere formality. And as her contraband was always dropped before she entered the atmosphere even a rigorous going over, as on this last occasion, would have revealed nothing.

Insofar as Eblis was concerned, you could land a battle fleet unobserved as long as it was well away from any of the widely spaced centres of population. There was Aero-Space Control, of a sort, but it had no radar and talked only when talked to.

The dreamy weed was grown and processed on quite a few of the Inner Worlds, the Federated Planets. As far as the Federation was concerned anybody could smoke the stuff who wished. It was regarded as a rather superior marihuana, the use of which had been legalized, for centuries, on practically every planet of the Federation. If any world government, inside or outside the Federation, cared to make its use illegal it was up to that government to enforce its own laws. The Federation couldn't care less, one way or the other, as long as it received whatever taxes and duties were due.

Grimes had his plan of campaign, such as it was, mapped out. He would land at Inferno Valley. He would tell Clavering, who had been made, some time ago, Planetary Commissioner on Eblis, that he was conducting a survey prior to the possible establishment of a naval base on the Hell Planet. He would use *Rim Malemute* for his excursions—she was a handy little brute and suitable for work inside an atmosphere—or, if necessary, he would hire air or ground transport. If Clavering were among the smugglers he would be liable to betray himself; if he were not he would afford every possible assistance to Grimes. The owner of a pleasure resort would profit rather than otherwise by the presence of recreation-hungry naval officers and ratings.

A subjective week after her lift-off from Port Last *Rim Malemute* was in orbit about Eblis. She circled the fiery world, her people gazing down in wonderment at the cloud envelope of black and brown and yellow smoke that, now and again, was driven by hurricane force winds to uncover the fire-belching volcanoes on the surface. The night side was even more spectacular, in a frightening sort of way, than the day side. It seemed that life-as-we-know-it could not possibly survive in that caldron of incandescent gases.

Williams asked wrily, "Sure we've come to the right place, Skipper."

"Quite sure, Commander Williams," Grimes told him. "Call Aero-Space Control, will you?"

"Rim Malemute to Aero-Space Control. *Rim Malemute* to Aero-Space Control. Do you read me? Over."

After the seventh call the Inferno Valley duty officer came through.

"Eblis Aero-Space Control here. Vessel calling, say again your name, please. Over."

"*Rim Malemute*. Repeat, *Rim Malemute*. Over."

"*Rim Malemute?* Aren't you the tug? Over."

Grimes took the microphone from Williams. "This is the Rim Worlds Naval Auxiliary *Rim Malemute*, requesting berthing instructions. Over."

"Have you been here before, *Rim Malemute?* The spaceport's at the eastern end of Inferno Valley." There was a long pause. "Latitude one three degrees, four five minutes north. Longitude oh, oh, oh degrees east *or* west. We reckon from the Inferno Valley meridian. The time here is 1149 hours, coming up for Mean Noon. Equation of Time zero as near as dammit. That any help to you? Over."

"Yes, thank you. Now, if you'll switch your beacon on. . . ."

"Give me time, man, give me time. Nobody was expecting you. On now."

"*Rim Malemute* to Aero-Space Control. Beacon signal coming in. We are almost directly above you. Have you any further instructions for us? Over."

"Yes. Listen carefully. Berth Number One—that's the pad furthest to the east—has *Sally Ann*. She's our ship. Berth Number Three—that's the one furthest to the west—has Trans-Galactic Clipper's cruise liner *Sobraon*. You should be able to get into Berth Number Two. I suppose you *are* the tug and not some dirty great battle cruiser with the same name? Over."

"Yes, we are the tug. Over."

"Watch the wind, *Rim Malemute*. In the Valley it is calm, but overhead we have west at seventy knots. Over."

"Thank you, Aero-Space Control. We are coming in. Over."

"We're coming in," repeated Williams. He cut the inertial drive and the little ship fell like a stone, applied vertical thrust to slow her descent only when her hull began to heat as she plunged into the outer atmosphere. He explained. "Have ter make it fast, Skipper. With all these bloody winds at umpteen knots we'll be all over the place unless we get downstairs in a hurry."

"Mphm," grunted Grimes, who had almost swallowed his pipe.

They were into the first cloud layer now, rolling black vapor slashed by dazzling lightning flashes. They were through it, and dropping through a stratum of clear air—and through turbulence that shook the tug like a terrier shaking a rat. Below them a cloudscape of fantastic castles in black and brown and yellow rushed up to meet them. Williams had no eye for the scenery; he was watching his radar altimeter and the shifting blip of the beacon signal. The ship shuddered as he applied lateral thrust to compensate for the fast drift to leeward.

They were under the cloud ceiling at last. Inferno Valley lay almost directly beneath them, a rift in the red rocks, a canyon, but one formed by geological upheaval than by erosion. To the north and to the south towered the volcanoes, classical cones, the smoke and steam from their craters streaming out almost horizontally. At the eastern end of the valley stood a great monolith, a fantastic needle of rock. The spaceport must be to the west of this formation.

Lower dropped *Rim Malemute* and lower, with Williams fighting to keep her in position relative to her landing site, with his officers calling out instrument readings in voices that, for all their studied calmness, betrayed fear. The nearer of the volcanoes emitted a great burst of smoke and incandescent molten matter and the dull *boom!* was felt and heard through the insulated hull. A shift of wind blew the *Malemute* away from the valley, at right angles to the rift—and once again she shuddered and complained in every member as lateral thrust drove her back on to her planned line of descent.

Then, quite suddenly, she was below the rim of the canyon. Below, deep, deep below, there was a silvery ribbon of water, the dark green of vegetation, the pastel colours of buildings. Below, looking from this altitude to be right alongside each other, were the metallic spires that were *Sally Ann* and *Sobraon*.

But there was room enough, and in this windless valley maneuvering was easy. Neatly, with no fuss and bother at all, Williams dropped *Rim Malemute* between the other two ships, in the exact centre of the triangle of brilliant red lights that marked his berth.

14

"Aero-Space Control to *Rim Malemute*. Leave your inertial drive on Stand By until your stays have been rigged and set up. Over."

"Stays?" asked Williams. *"Stays?"*

"Yes," Grimes told him. "Stays. Lengths of heavy wire rope, with bottle screws and springs. Necessary in case there's an exceptionally heavy earth tremor."

"And I suppose if there is one, before I've been tethered down, I have to get upstairs in a hurry."

"That's the drill."

Grimes, Williams, and *Rim Malemute's* officers looked out through the control room viewports. A man had come on to the apron, dressed in white shirt and shorts that were like a uniform, although they were not. He was giving orders to a squad of about a dozen natives. These looked as though they should have been carrying the traditional pitchforks instead of spikes and spanners. In appearance they were more like kangaroos than dinosaurs—but scaled kangaroos, with almost human heads. Almost human—their goatlike horns and the gleaming yellow tusks protruding from their mouths made it quite obvious that they were not. They wore no clothing, and their reptilian hides ranged in colour from a brown that was almost black to a yellow that was almost white. Three of them climbed up the *Malemute's* smooth sides, using the sucker pads on their hands and feet, carrying the ends of the wire cables after them with their prehensile tails. Swiftly, efficiently, they shackled these ends to conveniently situated towing lugs. They they scampered down to join their mates on the ground. The stays were stretched, set up taut. From the transceiver came the voice of Aero-Space Control, *"Rim Malemute,* you may shut down your engines and leave your ship at your discretion."

Grimes had been using binoculars to study the face of the man who had directed mooring operations. "Yes," he said at last. "That's Clavering. He's put on weight, lost that lean and hungry look, but he hasn't changed much."

He led the way down from the control room, followed by Williams. He was first down the still extruding ramp. Clavering came to meet him, threw him a sort of half salute. "Welcome to Inferno Valley, sir," he said not very enthusiastically. Then recognition dawned on his face. "Why, it's Commodore Grimes!" Then, with an attractive grin, "I'd have expected you to be in command of something bigger than *this!"*

"I'm not in command of *Rim Malemute,"* Grimes told him. "I'm just a passenger. This is Commander Williams, Captain Clavering, who had the dubious pleasure of bringing me here."

There was handshaking all round, then Clavering said, "Come to my office, and tell me what I can do for you."

Grimes and Williams looked about them curiously during their walk from the spaceport. It should have been gloomy in the deep ravine, with the murky yellow sky no more than a thin ribbon directly overhead, but it was not. The canyon walls—red, orange, banded with gold and silver—seemed to collect all the light that there was and to throw it back. Here and there on the sheer cliff faces vegetation had taken hold, static explosions of emerald green in which glowed sparks of blue and violet. Similar bushes grew from the firm, red sand that was the valley floor.

Two natives passed them, bound on some errand. They waved to Clavering, grinning hideously. He waved back. He said, "You get used to their horrendous appearance. They're good, cheerful workers. They like to be paid in kind rather than cash, in all the little luxuries that cannot be produced on this planet. Candy, they love. And they've acquired the taste for the more sickly varieties of lolly-water. Which reminds me—you are in from Port Last, aren't you? Did you see anything there of *Ditmar*? She brings my supplies in, and takes back the chemicals produced at my plant on the Bitter Sea, not far from here."

"I'm afraid she's going to be late," said Grimes. "She ran into all sorts of trouble with the Department of Navigation. Safety equipment was in a shocking state."

"I'm not surprised, Commodore. But you can't blame Captain Reneck entirely. His Owners seem to be a bunch of cheeseparing bastards. Still, he might have let me know he was delayed."

"You can't blame him for that, either," said Grimes. "The Post Office boys on Ultimo are playing up."

"Oh. And I shall have a strike on *my* hands if I try to pay my devils in cash instead of kind. Still, if worst comes to the worst I shall be able to do a deal of some kind with *Sobraon's* Catering Officer. Now, this is the Devil's Stew Pot that we're coming to. Between ourselves the story that the waters have marvellous rejuvenating properties is just a story— but a good soak and a good sweat never did anybody any harm."

The heat from the huge, circular, natural pool was almost overpowering even though they passed several meters from its rim. The people in it were not engaged in any violent physical activities. They just lay there in the shallows, only their faces, the breasts of the women and the protuberant bellies of both sexes appearing above the steaming surface.

"There are times," said Clavering, "when I wish, most sincerely, that *young* people could afford to come on these TG cruises."

"That one's not bad," said Grimes, nodding towards a woman who had just emerged from the water and who was walking slowly toward the next pool.

"Not bad at all," agreed Clavering. "She's old Silas Demarest's secretary, quote and unquote. You know—Demarest, the boss cocky of Galactic Metals. Now, this next bath, the Purgatorial Plunge, is not natural. Quite a few of my . . . er . . . customers give it a miss after they've sweated all the sin out of themselves. But it's amazing the extremes of cold that the human body can take after it's been well and truly heated.''

"Mphm." Grimes watched with appreciation as the naked girl dived into the clear, blue-green, icy water and propelled herself to the other side with swift, smooth strokes.

"And after the Purgatorial Pool you have the choice of swimming back to the Lucifer Arms—that's my hotel—in the River Styx, or walking along its banks. Or, if you're really keen, jogging along its banks. The temperature of the Styx is normal, by the way, what we refer to as pee-warm.''

The girl, Grimes saw, was swimming back, which was rather a pity, especially as she was a fast swimmer.

"Just around this bend you'll see the Lucifer Arms and the other buildings. Or 'inflations.' I had an architect staying here who tried to convince me that 'inflation' was a more correct word. This is earthquake country—this is an earthquake planet—and any normal construction wouldn't last long.''

And there, on the north bank of the Styx, was the Lucifer Arms. Imagine an igloo. Color it. Put another one beside it and color that, being careful to avoid a clash. Put another one beside the first two. Put one on top of the triangular base. And so on, and so on, and so on. . . .

Dome upon dome upon dome, and every one a

bubble of tough, stiffened plastic, its double skin filled with pressurized gas. It was as though some giant had emptied tons of detergent into the sluggishly flowing river and then stirred it violently so that the iridescent froth was flung up on to the bank. The edifice should have been an architectural nightmare—but, fantastically, it was not. Those soft-hued demispheres should have been in violent contrast to the harsh, red, towering walls of rock on either side of the rift valley—but in some weird way they matched the awe-inspiring scenery, enhanced it, even as did the ghost gums that Clavering had planted along the banks of the river, raised from saplings brought all the way from distant Earth. (But the management of TG Clippers, of course, had probably charged only nominal freight on them.)

The ex-Captain led the way to the hotel's main entrance, through the force screen into the airconditioned interior. It was only then that Grimes realized how sulphurous the hot air outside had been. It was a matter of contrasts. After the atmosphere of *Rim Malemute*, far too small a ship for any sort of voyage, even the natural air of Eblis had smelled and tasted good.

Clavering took Grimes and Williams to his office, itself a dome within the assemblage of domes. The three men seated themselves in very comfortable chairs that, too, were inflated plastic. A grinning devil, his scales highly polished, came to take their orders for drinks. Save for a tendency to hiss his sibilants his Galactic-English was very good.

Clavering sat back in his chair, which molded

itself to the contours of his body. Save for his almost white hair he had aged very little since Grimes had seen him last—how many years ago? He was as smooth and as smug as a well-fed cat—in that, he had changed.

After the native had brought the tray of drinks, in tall glasses misted with condensation, he asked, "And now, Commodore Grimes, just what can I do for you?"

15

"I thought you knew," said Grimes innocently.

"How the hell could I know?" countered Clavering. "I'm not a telepath."

"Didn't you get the letter, Captain?"

"What letter?"

"From the Admiralty."

"No. Was there supposed to be one?"

"Yes. I was shown a copy. But the mail services are getting worse than ever these days. The original will probably be in the mail brought by *Ditmar*, when she finally lifts off Ultimo."

"And just what is this famous letter about?"

"The base."

"What base?"

"Sorry, I was forgetting that you don't know. I'll put you in the picture. The Space Lords of the Confederacy, with a surplus of the taxpayers' money to play with, have decided that it might be a good idea to establish a naval base on Eblis."

"What in the Universe for? It would have no strategic value whatsoever."

"Just what I tried to tell them, Captain Clavering. But ours not to reason why, and all the rest of it."

"I suppose not." Then, "I'm glad to see you
again after all these years, Commodore Grimes, but
you might have let me know that you were coming.
An ETA would have been useful. As it was, you just
appeared out of nowhere and, between ourselves,
young Lingard who's supposed to be in charge of
Aero-Space Control isn't the brightest. He should
have told you to stay in orbit until sunset or dawn,
when there's always an hour or so of flat calm. He
should have asked you if you wanted a pilot in. I do
the piloting, as a matter of fact. I go up in one of *Sally
Ann's* boats and board outside the atmosphere."

"Keeping your hand in. . . ."

"Yes." Then Clavering returned to his original
complaint. "I know that the Navy always does as it
damn' well pleases, but an ETA would have been
useful."

"You'd have got one," lied Grimes, with a warning glance at Williams, "if the Carlotti gear hadn't
gone on the blink. I'm afraid that the poor little
Malemute's showing her age. If it's not one thing
broken down, it's something else." Then, as a sop to
Rim Malemute's skipper, "Of course, she's very
hardworking."

"But this base, Commodore," said Clavering.
"The idea's crazy. Eblis is absolutely unsuitable.
There's a shortage of suitable landing sites, and the
climate is quite impossible, and. . . ."

"You made out all right, Captain." Grimes
smiled. "And look at the trade that *you'd* be doing,
as owner of the only recreational facilities on the
planet."

268

"And look at the headaches I'd be getting! The natives spoiled by the big money, or its equivalent, splashed around by a spendthrift government. Brawls in my bars. . . ."

"Come, come. I'll not say that our officers and ratings are fit and proper personnel for a Sunday School Treat—but they are quite well behaved."

"They may be, Commodore, but are the tourists? I can just imagine it. Mr. Silas Q. Moneybags is staying here with his latest blonde secretary. A handsome young lieutenant, all prettied up in his go-ashore uniform, does a line with the blonde. Mr. Moneybags, after a drink or three too many, takes a swing at the lieutenant. Oh, no, Commodore. That sort of carry on is not for me if I can possibly avoid it."

"Mphm. I see your point, Captain. But I was sent here to make a survey, and a survey I have to make. To begin with, I suppose you have Eblis pretty well charted?"

"Of course. I was a navigator before I became a hotel manager. Suppose you and Commander Williams come with me to my map room."

"Thank you," said Grimes.

The map room was in another of the plastic bubbles. It contained a mounted globe, a huge table upon which flat charts could be spread, a projector, and a wall screen.

Clavering went first to the sphere, sent it spinning with a touch of a finger, slowed its rotation with another touch, stopped it. "Here," he said, "is

Inferno Valley. A typical rift formation, as you will already have realized. To the north we have the Greak Smokies, and to the south the Erebus Alps. North of the Smokies you find the Painted Badlands—and the sandstorms there can strip even one of my armorplated devils to bare bones in minutes. South of the Alps there's mountain range after mountain range—the Devil's Torches, the Infernal Beacons, the Lucifers. . . . He rotated the globe twenty degrees. ''To the west of Inferno Valley there's the Bitter Sea. Our chemical extraction plant is there. Even if the tourist trade died on us—and it shows no signs of ever doing so—we'd get by. And to the north we still have the Smokies, and to the south the Torches, the Beacons and the Lucifers.'' The globe rotated again. ''And here there's a quite remarkable formation, stretching practically from pole to pole. The Satan's Barrier Range. Worth visiting just to see the fantastic rock formations, such as the Valley of the Winds and the Devil's Organ Pipes. When conditions are right you'd swear that some supernatural being was playing a gigantic organ—a little light music for Walpurgis Nacht.

''West of the Barrier there're the Fire Forests and the Burning Pits. The Fire Forests are . . . clumps of young, new volcanoes, and their number grows every year. The Burning Pits are just what their name implies. Further west still, and we begin to pick up the foothills of the east-west ranges—the Great Smokies, the Torches and all the rest of them. There are, of course, valleys like this one, but smaller. There's nothing that could accommodate a Base, with its barracks and workshops and repair yards.''

"Mphm. Quite a world you have here, Captain Clavering. I suppose you run tours from Inferno Valley for your customers?"

"Yes. Unluckily the Organ Pipes tour was a couple of days ago, and my air cars are now undergoing maintenance. You will appreciate that the abrasive winds make this essential after every outing. I'll not be running another tour until *Macedon* comes in. *Sobraon*, of course, lifts off first thing tomorrow morning."

"Taking her out?"

"Yes. Her Master's newly appointed and would like to see the Eblis pilotage both ways, arrival and departure, before he makes a stab at it himself. And now you really must excuse me. There's always something to be done around a place like this. But you'll have dinner with us tonight, of course. Sally Ann will be wanting to see you again. You too, of course, Commander Williams, are invited." He paused. "Come to that, why don't you and all *Rim Malemute's* people stay at the Lucifer Arms? I've plenty of accommodation."

"And I'm entitled to reasonable expenses," said Grimes.

Clavering laughed. "I should have made it clear that I want you as non-paying guests. But I'm not averse to taking the government's money."

"And I'm not averse," said Grimes, "to having some small percentage of what I pay in income tax and customs duty spent on my comfort."

And had a flicker of apprehension showed on Clavering's face when Grimes used the words "customs duty"?

Damn it all! thought the Commodore, *I'm neither a policeman nor a customs officer.*

Then he remembered young Pleshoff, whose career had been ruined, and Peter Fellini and Inga Telfer, who were dead.

16

The dining room of the Lucifer Arms was yet
another plastic hemisphere, but a huge one. Clavering and Sally, his wife, had their table in the exact
centre of the circular floor. It was on a low dais,
raised above the level of the others so that the ex-
Captain could oversee everything that was going on.
Not that his supervision was really necessary; his
devils, looking more than ever like refugees from a
black humor cartoon in their stiff white shirts, black
ties and black jackets, were superbly trained, attentive without being obtrusive. And there were three
human headwaiters, circulating slowly among the
diners, watching everything.

Grimes enjoyed his meal. For almost as long as he
could remember he had liked highly spiced, exotic
foods, and every item on the menu was either deviled
or flambèed—or both. Williams, who preferred
good plain cooking, was not so happy—but to judge
by his rate of consumption he found nothing at all
wrong with the excellent chilled hock. Neither did
Captain Gillings of *Sobraon* who, with his Chief
Officer Mr. Tait, made up the party. So far he was

showing no effects, but—*Any moment now!* thought Grimes. And—*It's none of* my *business.*

Yet when Gillings put his hand firmly over the top of his empty glass, saying, "I lift off at dawn," Clavering persuaded him to accept a refill, remarking, "I'm taking your ship up for you, Captain. As long as *I'm* on the ball in the morning." Mrs. Clavering, a tall, very attractive blonde, looked as though she were about to interfere, especially when she saw that her husband's glass was also being refilled. She asked Grimes rather pointedly, "What are the rules about drinking in the Navy, Commodore?"

Grimes said, "It all depends. Sometimes you know that you can afford to relax, at other times you know that you can't. Mphm. But drink is not the major problem. You can always tell if a man is under the influence. With other drugs you can't tell if a man's judgment has been seriously impaired. Not so long ago—in my civilian capacity as Rim Runners' Chief Astronautical Superintendent—I had to try to sort out a most distressing business. The Third Officer of one of our ships had been among those involved in a dreamy weed orgy. The next morning, apparently quite normal, he was testing the gear prior to his vessel's lift off from Port Last. The inertial drive, which had been given a trial run by the engineers after maintenance, was on Stand By. The officer noticed this—and thought it would be a good idea to take the ship up, himself, for a joyride."

"And what happened?" asked Sally Clavering.

"General alarm and despondency. Luckily there was nobody hurt, and no serious damage. The young man, I'm afraid, will have to serve a jail term—the Rim Confederacy takes a very dim view of drugs in general. And his spacegoing career is ruined."

"If your government," said the TG Clipper captain, "weren't so many years behind the times that sort of thing wouldn't happen. In the Federated Planets we accept the consciousness-expanding drugs. We know that there are some people affected more strongly than others, just as there are some people more strongly affected by alcohol than others. On Austral—my home planet—a smoker has to take out a license and is subjected to various physical and psychological tests. He knows just what effect marihuana, dreamy weed or anything similar will have on him, and regulates his activities accordingly. In my own case, for example, I know that if I were enjoying a pipe instead of Captain Clavering's excellent wine I should be, no more than two standard hours after the last inhalation, perfectly capable of taking my ship into or out of any spaceport in the Galaxy—more capable, in fact, than if I had not smoked. This Third Officer of yours was unlucky."

"You can say that again, Captain Gillings," agreed Grimes. He looked casually around the table. Sally Clavering was showing interest in the conversation. So was Mr. Tait, Gillings' Chief Officer. Williams looked as though he were interested only in the wine. And Clavering was suddenly taking great interest in a party of rather noisy revellers six tables away.

He said, "I hope those people don't carry on like that aboard your ship, Captain Gillings."

"Not all the time, Captain Clavering. They're usually quite quiet at breakfast."

"Black coffee and two aspirins, I suppose. Talking of coffee, shall we adjourn to the Grotto? I've some rather decent Altairian Dragon's Blood that we could have as a liqueur."

He got up from the table and, as soon as his wife and his guests were on their feet, led the way from the dining room, pausing slightly now and again to exchange salutations with the people at the other tables.

A short tunnel led to the Grotto, its walls coloured and shaped in the likenesses of rough granite. Grimes had to put his hand out to convince himself that they were not granite and was almost surprised by the soft spongy texture under his fingers. In the Grotto itself amazingly realistic stalactites hung from the high ceiling, and stalagmites grew upwards from the floor. But if there should be an earth tremor there would be no danger of frail human flesh being crushed and torn by falling masses of jagged limestone. Should, by any chance, a stalactite be shaken adrift from its overhead anchorage it would float gently downwards like the plastic balloon that in actuality, it was. Nonetheless, the effect was convincing, enhanced by the dim green and blue lighting, by musical trickling of water somewhere in the background.

They sat around a table that could have been a slab of waterworn limestone, on surprisingly comfortable chairs simulating the same material. A devil brought a tray with coffee pot and cups, another devil the teardrop decanter and the slim glasses. Sally Clavering poured the coffee, her husband the liqueur.

"Here's to crime," said Grimes, raising his glass.

"An odd toast, Commodore," said Clavering.

"A very old one, Captain."

"It all depends," said Captain Gillings, whose speech was becoming a little slurred, "on what you mean by crime."

"Too," said Williams, who enjoyed an occasional philosophical argument, "one has to distinguish between crime and sin."

"Smuggling, for example," said Grimes, "is a crime, but is it a sin?"

"Depends on what you smuggle," said Gillings.

"Too right," agreed Williams.

"Take gambling," said Clavering a little desperately. "It's a crime—I mean, it's classed as a crime—when the State doesn't get its rake-off. But as long as the government gets its cut it's perfectly all right."

"I 'member once on Elshinore . . ." began Gillings. "Ticket in Shtate Lottery . . . only sheventeen off million creditsh. . . ."

"I always think," said Grimes, "that the people of these very agricultural planets, like Elsinore and Ultimo, need such outlets as gambling and, perhaps, drug-taking. The essentially rural worlds tend to be more—sinful, shall we say?—more sinful than the heavily industralized ones."

"Who shaid gambling wash a shin, Commodore?" asked Gillings.

277

"It's only a sin," said Clavering thoughtfully, "if somebody else, somebody apart from the gambler himself is hurt. That can be said about most crimes, so-called."

"Take forgery," contributed Williams. *(Blast you!* thought Grimes. *Why must you go changing the subject?)* "Take forgery. S'pose I print a million Ten Credit notes. S'pose they're all perfect. Undetectable. I win. But who loses?"

"I'll go into partnership with you, C'mander Williamsh," said Gillings. "When d'we shtart?"

"Time we started getting back to the ship, sir," said Mr. Tait, looking pointedly at his watch.

"A nightcap, Captain Gillings?" asked Clavering.

"Thank you, Captain Clavering. I will take jusht one li'l hair o' the dog thash bitin' me. After all, it'sh a long worm that hash no turning. Thank you. Thank you. Your very good health, shir. An' yoursh, Mishess Clavering. An' yoursh, Commodore Grimesh. An' yoursh, Commander Williamsh. An' . . . an'. . . . Shorry, Mishter Tait. Glash's empty. Musta 'vaporated. Very dry climate here. Very dry. . . ."

Somehow Tait got his captain out of the Grotto. Mrs. Clavering looked at her husband angrily. "You know he can't take it. That Dragon's Blood on top of what he had before and with dinner." She looked at Grimes. "I'm sorry, Commodore. But this sort of thing makes me angry."

"It's not as though he were taking his ship up himself," said Clavering.

"It makes no difference. As *you* were always telling me, before you came ashore, the Master is *always* responsible for his ship. You should have known better than to encourage him."

"He'll be all right in the morning, Sally." He yawned. "Time I was getting some shut-eye myself. And I'm sure that you and Commander Williams must be tired, Commodore. I'll show you to to your rooms."

"Thank you, Captain. Oh, I'd rather like to see you take *Sobraon* up tomorrow. Both of us would, in fact. Do you think you could have us called in time?"

"Surely. You can come along for the ride, in fact. I put her in orbit, then my boat will pick us up and bring us back. I'll tell the devil in charge of your level to call you in good time. What do you want with your morning trays? Tea? Coffee? Or whatever?"

"Coffee," said Grimes and "Tea," said Williams.

Clavering took them to a lift shaft that was one of the very few really rigid structural members in the hotel, accompanied them to their levels, and then took them to their rooms. Williams, who was not quite sober, looked at the inside of his hemispherical sleeping compartment and said that he wanted Eskimo Nell to keep his bed warm. Clavering told him that the devils who looked after the bedrooms were female devils. Williams said that, on second thoughts, he would prefer to sleep alone. He vanished through the circular doorway.

279

Grimes said goodnight to Clavering then went into his own bedroom. It looked to be very comfortable, with an inflated bed and matching chair, a shower and toilet recess and—the only solid furnishing—a refrigerator. Suddenly he felt thirsty. He looked in the refrigerator, found fruit and several bottles of mineral water, together with plastic tumblers. He opened one of the bottles, poured himself a drink. But he only half finished it. It was deliciously cold but, after the first few swallows, its flavor was . . . wrong. The water from the tap in the shower recess was lukewarm and tasted of sulphur, but it was better. Grimes drank copiously—the dinner had been conducive to thirst—then undressed and got into the soft, resilient bed.

No sooner had his head hit the pillow than there was an earth tremor, not severe but quite noticeable. He grinned to himself and muttered, "I don't need rocking." Nor did he.

17

Like most men who are or who have been in active command Grimes possessed a built-in alarm clock. This woke him promptly at 0500 hours Local, the time at which the domestic devil was supposed to be calling him, with coffee. Although Grimes had awakened he was in a rather confused state and it took him many seconds to work out where he was and what he was supposed to be doing. He was on Eblis. He was shut up in a pneumatic plastic igloo. He was supposed to be aboard *Sobraon* before she lifted off at 0600 hours. He wanted his coffee. Even when there had been no night before the morning after he wanted his coffee to start the day with. He thought about coffee the way that it should be—hot as hell, black as sin and strong as the devil. Talking about devils—where the hell was the lazy devil who should have called him?

Grimes found a bell push among the inflated padding that backed the bed. He pushed it. He pushed it again. He pushed it a third time. Eventually the plug-like door opened and the chambermaid, if you could call her that, came in. The white frilly cap

looked utterly absurd perched on top of her horns.
She asked in a well modulated voice, with only the
merest hint of croak or hiss, "You rang, sir?"

"No. My physiotherapist told me that I should
exercise my right thumb more."

"My apologies for the intrusion, sir." She turned
to go. The long claws of her kangaroo-like feet
indented the padded floor.

"Wait. I was joking. Word was left for me to be
called at five, with coffee. It is now 0515."

"Nobody told me, sir. Do you wish coffee?"

"Yes, please."

"Black, sir, or white? With sugar or without? Or
with mintsweet, or lemonsweet, or honey? And do
you wish toast, sir, or a hot roll? With butter, or with
one or more of our delicious preserves? Or with
butter and preserves?"

"Just coffee. In a pot. A big one. Better bring a
cup as well. Sugar. No milk. Nothing to eat."

"Are you sure that you would not care for the full
breakfast, sir? Fruit, a variety of cereals, eggs to
order, ham or bacon or sausages. . . ."

"No!" He softened this to "No, thank you."
After all, the demon-girl was doing her best. "Just
coffee. Oh, and you might look in the room next
door to see if Commander Williams is up. He wanted
tea, I think."

Grimes showered hastily, depilated, then dressed.
While he was doing this latter the coffee arrived. It
was good coffee. After he had finished his first cup
he thought he had better see how Williams was
getting on.

The tray, with its teapot and accessories, was on the Commander's bedside table. The commander was still in the bed. He was snoring loudly and unmusically.

"Commander Williams!" said Grimes. "Commander Williams!" snapped Grimes. "Commander Williams!" roared Grimes.

In any Service it is an unwritten law that an officer must not be touched in any way to awaken him— even when the toucher is superior in rank to the touchee. Grimes knew this—but he wanted Williams on his feet, *now*. He took hold of the other man's muscular shoulder, shook it. Williams interrupted his snoring briefly and that was all. Grimes hammered on the headboard of Williams' bed—but it, like everything else except the refrigerator, was pneumatically resilient, emitted no more than a soft, slapping sound.

Grimes thought of hammering the refrigerator door with something hard and heavy and had his right shoe half off before he thought of a better idea. Presumably this cold box, like the one in his room, would contain a few bottles of mineral water.

It did. There were six bottles, and five of them were empty, put back after they were finished by Williams, who had a small ship man's necessary tidiness. Grimes pulled the seal of the sixth bottle, inverted it over the Commander's head. The icy fluid gurgled out, splashed over hair and face and bare chest and shoulders.

Williams' eyes opened. He said, slowly and distinctly, "Mr. Timmins, you will fix the thermostat *at once.* This is a ship, Mr. Timmins, a *ship*—not an orbital home for superannuated polar bears. I want her warm as a busty blonde's bottom, not cold as the Commodore's heart.''

"Williams, wake up, damn you!"

"Brragh."

It was hopeless. And Williams' sleep was far deeper than could be accounted for by the previous night's drinking. He had taken nothing like as much as Captain Gillings—and, presumably, *he* was up. Those bottles of mineral water, only one of which Grimes had no more than tasted, five of which Williams nad quaffed. . . .

But who . . .?

And why . . .?

Grimes looked at his watch. If he hurried he would get to the spaceport before *Sobraon* lifted. He tried to hurry, but considerable local knowledge was required to find a quick way out of the vast honeycomb that the Lucifer Arms resembled. At last he was clear of the building and running along the path of coarse red sand beside the Styx. It was dark still, it would be some time before Inferno Valley received the benefit of the rising sun. But there was light enough from the luminescent lichenous growths that grew, here and there, on the granite cliffs. Past the Purgatorial Pool he ran, past the Devil's Stewpot, blundering through the white, acrid fog that, at this hour of the morning, shrouded its surface.

And there were the ships at last—Clavering's *Sally Ann* in the background, dwarfed by the towering Devil's Phallus, and *Sobraon,* hiding with her bulk the little *Rim Malemute.* The TG Clipper's atmosphere running lights were on, and at the very tip of her needle-pointed stem an intensely bright red light was winking, the signal that she was ready for lift off. Loud in the morning calm was the irritable warming-up mumble of her inertial drive. Well clear of her vaned landing gear the mooring gang—the unmooring gang—was standing in little groups. The last airlock door was shut, the boarding ramp in.

The note of the liner's inertial drive deepened, became throbbingly insistent. A siren howled eerily. Then she was lifting, slowly, carefully. She was lifting, and her drive sounded like the hammers of hell as it dragged her massive tonnage up to the distant ribbon of yellow that was the sky.

She lifted—then suddenly checked, but there was no change in the beat of her engines, no diminution of the volume of noise. Yet she hung there, motionless, and those on the ground, human and native, started to run along the valley toward Grimes.

There was a sound like that of a breaking fiddle string—a fiddle string inches in diameter plucked to destruction by a giant, ship-sized giant, a ship. . . . *Sobraon*, suddenly freed, surged upwards, and astern of her the broken ends of the mooring cable that had fouled one of her vanes lashed out like whips, striking sparks from the granite rocks.

And *Rim Malemute*, whose mooring wire it was that had been snagged, teetered for long seconds on two feet of her tripedal landing gear, teetered—and toppled.

"Cor!" muttered somebody, "they haven't half made a mess of the poor little bitch."

Grimes looked at him. It was *Rim Malemute's*

shipkeeping officer, who had turned out to watch the big TG Clipper's lift off.

The Commodore said, "You're a witness. Come with me to the control tower and we'll slap a complaint on the Duty Controller's desk before he has time to think of sueing us for having our lines too close to *Sobraon's* stern vanes."

"But he can't, sir. The Port Captain himself saw the moorings set up."

"Port Captains," Grimes told him, "are like the kings in olden days. They can do no wrong."

18

The Control Tower was a shack on stilts and had little in the way of electronic equipment—just a normal spacetime transceiver, a Carlotti transceiver and, logically enough for this planet, a seismograph. The Duty Aero-Space Control Officer was little more than a boy, and a badly frightened boy at that. He looked around with a start as Grimes and the *Malemute's* Third Engineer burst in. He said, in a shaken voice, "Did you see that, sir? Did you see that?"

"Too right I saw it!" Grimes told him. "Stick a piece of paper in your typewriter and take this down. Ready? I, John Grimes, Commodore, Rim Worlds Naval Reserve, senior officer of the Rim Worlds Navy on Eblis, hereby lodge a complaint, as follows. Got all that? At 0600 hours this morning—put the date in, will you?—the cruise line *Sobraon*, under the pilotage of Captain Clavering, Port Captain, Inferno Valley, fouled the moorings of the Rim Worlds Naval Auxiliary Vessel *Rim Malemute*, as a result of which *Rim Malemute* sustained severe damage, the extent of which has yet to be determined. I, Commodore John Grimes, hold the Inferno Valley port authorities responsible for this accident. That's all. Give it to me, and I'll sign it. Take copies and let me have three.''

"But, sir, it was an accident. I saw it too. When *Sobraon's* vane fouled *Rim Malemute's* moorings Captain Clavering had to keep on going. The ship was off balance. If he'd tried to land there's have been a shocking disaster.''

"I *said* it was an accident,'' stated Grimes. "But that has no bearing at all on the question of legal liability. Somebody will have to pay for the repairs to the *Malemute*. I suppose that it will be Lloyd's, as usual.''

But was it an accident? Grimes asked himself. This *Sobraon* was practically a sister ship to Clavering's own *Sally Ann*, his last space-going command. Too, Clavering had piloted *Sobraon* inwards. He would know the second/foot/tons developed by her inertial drive. As Port Captain he would know, too, the breaking strain of *Rim Malemute's* moorings. His motive? Plain enough. He didn't want Grimes ranging far and wide over the surface of Eblis, ostensibly conducting a survey. Deliberately, knowing Gillings' weakness, he had got the TG Clipper's Master drunk the night before lift off. And Gillings, knowing that he was morally as well as legally to blame for the alleged accident, would tend to back up Clavering in any story that did not show him and his pilot in a bad light. After all, insofar as his owners were concerned *he* was there, and *they* were not.

Just then Clavering came through on the transceiver. His face, in the little screen, was surprisingly calm. Behind him, Gillings seemed to have aged years in as many minutes. "*Sobraon* to Eblis Aero-Space Control . . . I don't think we sustained any damage, but I'm putting the ship in orbit until we're sure. Expect me when you see me. Over."

"Commodore Grimes is here, sir."

"Put him on, will you? Good morning, Commodore. I'm afraid we damaged your *Malemute*. I saw her come a clanger in the rear vision screen. I'm sorry about that."

"So am I," Grimes said.

"I'm Lloyd's Agent on Eblis. I'll survey *Malemute* as soon as I get back."

"That's uncommonly decent of you," said Grimes.

"Don't take it so hard, Commodore. Excuse me, please. I've some pilotage to do. Over and out."

"Mphm," grunted Grimes. After this unsatisfactory conversational exchange he could continue with his thoughts. There was the failure, the deliberate failure, he was sure, to have Grimes and Williams called so that they could be in *Sobraon's* control room during lift off. There were the bottles of drugged mineral water—very tempting after a thirst inducing meal—in the bedroom refrigerators. Of course, he did not know that the mineral water had been drugged, but it certainly looked that way. He should have kept a sample—but what good would that have been? On this world there were no police, no forensic laboratories. Clavering was the law—such as it was.

Clavering came back on the NST transceiver. "In

orbit," he announced. "The Chief Officer's making an inspection now. Is Commodore Grimes still with you?"

"Grimes here."

"For your report, Commodore, the wind caught us just as we were lifting."

"There wasn't any wind, Captain Clavering. I saw the whole thing happen."

"Oh, there wouldn't be any wind at ground level. But there are some odd eddies in the higher levels of the canyon."

"As low as only one hundred meters up?"

"Yes."

And you're the expert on this bloody world, thought Grimes. *Your word'd be better than mine if I tried to raise any kind of a stink.*

"For the remainder of your stay on Eblis," went on Clavering, "you and your people must stay free of charge at my hotel. I cannot help feeling that I'm to blame for what happened."

Too right you are, thought Grimes.

"We'll talk things over as soon as I get back."

We'll do just that, thought Grimes.

"I'll be seeing you, then."

"I'll be seeing you, Captain Clavering," said Grimes, trying to inject the slightest touch of menace into his voice. If he got Clavering worried he might start making mistakes.

And—*Damn it all,* thought Grimes, *I'm not a policeman!*

He said to the Duty Officer, "Ring the hotel, please, and see if Commander Williams is available."

Commander Williams, it seemed, was not. When he finally did wake up, thought Grimes, he'd be sorry that he hadn't stayed asleep. He loved his little *Malemute* as other men loved a woman.

19

Late in the morning Williams broke surface. When he heard what had happened to his ship he snapped from a muzzy semiconsciousness to a state of energetic alertness with amazing rapidity. As soon as he was dressed he hurried to the spaceport to assess the damage.

Grimes waited for him in the spacious lounge of the Lucifer Arms that now, after the cruise liner's departure, was almost deserted. Sally Clavering found him there. She sat down, facing him over the small table with its coffee service, said. "I heard what happened, Commodore."

"You probably heard it happen," said Grimes, who was in a bad mood. "There was quite a crash."

"But Ian's such a *good* shiphandler."

Grimes relented slightly. He had always found it hard to speak unkindly to really attractive women. He said, "The best of us have our off days. And, sooner or later, accidents just have to happen."

"Do you think it *was* an accident?" she asked.

"Mphm," grunted Grimes noncommitally.

She said, "I'm worried, Commodore. I've a

feeling—it's more than just a feeling—that Ian's got himself into some sort of trouble. Over the past year or so he's . . . changed. I've asked him, more than once, what it is, but he just laughs it off."

"Money trouble?" asked Grimes.

She laughed. "That's the least of our worries. I was as you know, *Sally Ann's* Purser—and now I'm ashore I carry on pursering. I keep the books for the hotel and all the rest of it. I hope you don't think that I'm boasting when I say that we're doing *very* nicely."

"Income Tax?"

"No. Really, Commodore, we have it made. Eblis is one of the Rim Worlds, and legally speaking is part of the Confederacy, but *we*, *Sally Ann's* crew, were the first settlers, the only permanent settlers. How did our lawyer put it? 'You're *of*, but not *in*, the Confederacy.' Sooner or later the Grand Council of the Confederacy will get around to passing laws to bring us in properly, so we have to pay taxes, and duty on everything we import. What's holding up such legislation is the squabbling over which of the Rim Worlds shall take us under its wing—Lorn or Faraway, Ultimo or Thule. Another complicating factor, which we shall drag in if we have to, is that *Sally Ann*, still in commission, is under Federation registration, and all of us, *Sally Ann's* original crew, are still Federation citizens."

"Complicated," admitted Grimes.

"Yes, isn't it? Of course, if the Navy decides that it *must* have a base here there's not much that we can do about it." She smiled. "But we have reduced rates at the hotel for legislators. That should help.''

''You shouldn't have told me that.''

''Everybody knows. Everybody knows, too, that a holiday here would be impossibly expensive if our profits were eaten away by taxes. Our guests from the Rim Worlds aren't in the same financial brackets as those in the cruise liners, from the Federation's planets. The next cruise ship in will be *Macedon*. While she's still here Ian will be taking *Sally Ann* to Ultimo to pick up a large party of Rim Worlders. A religious convention, as a matter of fact.''

''Odd,'' commented Grimes. ''This is hardly the sort of world to inspire the fear of hell fire.''

''It is in parts, Commodore, make no mistake about that. But these people who're coming don't belong to any of the old religions. They're members of some new cult or faith or whatever. What do they call themselves? The Gateway? Something like that.''

''All religions are gateways, I suppose, or make out that they're gateways—gateways to . . . something.'' He tried to steer the conversation back on to its original track. ''With all this trade I can't see how you or Captain Clavering have anything to worry about.''

''That's it, Commodore. We shouldn't have any worries. But Ian's been . . . odd lately. Forgive me for suggesting it, but I thought that you, as a fellow shipmaster, might be able to pull him out of it. He'll tell you things that he wouldn't tell me.''

Is there a Marriage Guidance Counsellor in the house? thought Grimes. He said, ''Just a phase, probably. All marriages pass through them. There are times when Sonya—you must meet her some time—when Sonya and I are hardly on speaking terms. But we get over it." *Another woman?* he asked himself. *Or . . .?*

She read his thoughts, partially at least. She said, "It's not another woman. He has his opportunities, running a resort like this. He may have taken an occasional opportunity. But his . . . his secrecy is worse between ships, at times like this when the hotel is empty. There's something on his mind. He hardly slept at all last night, and when he did sleep he was muttering to himself. And it wasn't a woman's name, either. It was, I think, just technicalities. 'Thrust' came into it. And 'breaking strain'."

"Mphm. Just a technician's nightmare. I get 'em myself sometimes." He remembered the dream that Williams must have experienced when he, Grimes, tried in vain to awaken him. "So do other people. Oh, by the way, do you bottle your own mineral water?"

She looked surprised at the abrupt change of subject, then said, "Yes. As a matter of fact we do. We have a small plant on the bank of the river, the only river, running into the Bitter Sea. Its water's not quite as rich in assorted chemicals as the Sea itself. Rather an acquired taste, actually, although it's supposed to have all sorts of medicinal qualities. The tourists drink it religiously. We import soft drinks too—but they're mainly for the devils, who enjoy anything as long as it's really sweet."

"I had some of your own mineral water last night,

when I turned in. I thought it tasted a bit . . . odd.''

"It most certainly does, Commodore. I never touch it myself. But the bottling plant is one of Ian's hobbies.'' She lapsed into a short, brooding silence. "If ever a man *should* be happy, it's him.''

"Men are unwise and curiously planned,'' quoted Grimes.

"You can say that again, Commodore. But here comes your Commander Williams. He looks as though *he* has real worries. I'll leave you to him.''

Williams dropped into the chair vacated by Sally Clavering, so heavily that Grimes feared that he would burst it. He said, "She's had it. She's really had it, Skipper. The inertial drive unit sheered its holding-down bolts. The Mannschenn Drive looks like one of those mobile sculptures—an' about as much bloody use! Even the boats are in a mess—the inertial drive units again. The work boat is the least badly damaged.''

"Radio gear?''

"We can fix the NST transceiver, I think, but not the Carlotti. We haven't the spares. But the *Malemute* herself . . . we have to get her sitting up properly before we can start any major repairs, an' there's no heavy lifting gear on the bloody planet. We could do it by using a tug—but *Rim Malemute* is the only tug we have in commission—*had* in commission—on the whole bloody Rim. Oh, yes, there's *Rim Husky*, but she's been laid up for so long that she's just part of the Port Edgell scenery—an' at her best she couldn't pull a soldier off her sisters!''

"We can ask Captain Clavering to hook on to the *Malemute* when he takes his *Sally Ann* out."

"Yes, we can, I suppose. He's *very* good at towing, isn't he? Ha, ha! An' when'll that be, Skipper?"

"Not until *Macedon's* arrived here. Mphm. I doubt if he'll come at it. Too much chance of damaging Macedon."

"He didn't mind damaging *Sobraon*. Although I did hear, from that young puppy in Aero-Space Control, that she got away with no worse than a few scratches an' some dented fairing. Clavering's on his way back down from orbit now, an' Captain Gillings, the pride of TG Clippers, is on *his* way rejoicing. What a pair! What a bloody pair! He an' Clavering. . . ."

"You weren't too bright yourself this morning."

Williams grinned ruefully. "No, I wasn't, was I? Do you know what I think it was?" He obviously did not expect that his story would be believed. "I had one helluva thirst when I turned in, and all that was in the 'fridge was a half dozen bottles of lolly water. It tasted like it'd been drunk before, but it was cold and wet. You know, Skipper. I think it must have gone bad."

"You could be right," said Grimes, "although not in the way you mean."

20

Clavering came in from orbit. As soon as his boat had landed he sought out Grimes. He said, "I'm afraid I made a mess of your *Rim Malemute*."

"You did just that, Captain Clavering. I take it you've seen my letter on the subject?"

"I have, Commodore. Don't you think it was rather unnecessary?"

"No. I represent the Rim Worlds Navy, and when one of their ships is damaged I have to make sure that the person responsible, or his insurance company, foots the bill for repairs."

Clavering grinned without mirth. "I suppose you read the copy of Inferno Valley Port Regulations I had put aboard your *Malemute?* One of the rules is that anybody who lands on this planet does so at his own risk. But we're both of us spacemen, Commodore. Suppose you enjoy your holiday here, and let the lawyers argue about who pays whom for what." His grin was friendly now. "I'm sure that you and Commander Williams will join me in a drink to show that there's no hard feelings."

"Smoke the pipe of peace," said Grimes.

Clavering looked at him, hard, but Grimes kept

his face expressionless, thinking, *I shouldn't mind betting that he could produce a pipe of dreamy weed if it were called for*.

A devil brought cold drinks. The Commodore sipped his, then said, "I'm not sure that I should be having this. And I'm sure that Williams should lay off the grog after his effort last night. We both of us slept in. Of course, if we'd been called on time. . . ."

Clavering flushed—guiltily? He said, "I seem to be doing nothing else but apologize. It was my fault. I should have seen to it personally that your level devil understood the instructions. I should have checked up on you before I left the hotel. But I overslept myself, and had to rush down to the ship almost as soon as I was out of bed. With these big brutes the only safe time to lift off or land is during the dawn or sunset lull."

"And even then it's not all that bloody safe," remarked Williams.

"Nothing is safe, Commander, ever. You should know that by this time."

"If anything can go wrong, it will," contributed Grimes.

"You said it, Commodore. It's really surprising that things don't go wrong more often."

"Mphm. And now, Captain Clavering much as we're enjoying your hospitality I have to remind you that we're here on business."

"Business?" Was there a flicker of fear in Clavering's eyes?

"Yes. This survey for the projected base. Had you

forgotten? I was wondering if we could hire transport from you."

Clavering did his best to look apologetic. "Normally I'd be only too pleased to let you have something suitable, Commodore. But this request of yours comes at an awkward time. Apart from *Sally Ann's* boats I have only two heavy-duty atmosphere craft. They were both used extensively for tours during *Sobraon's* stay on Eblis, and with maintenance staff working flat out they'll be ready for use again just when *Macedon* comes in."

"What about *Sally Ann's* boats?"

"Once again, out of the question. I've just finished getting them up to the required standard for my charter trip. You know as well as I do—better than I do, probably—what sticklers for regulations the Department of Navigation Surveyors are at Port Last, and that's where I shall be going. I don't want to be held up the same as *Ditmar* has been."

"I suppose not. How about ground cars?"

"We don't have any—not for passenger transport. We have the trucks bringing chemicals from our plant on the Bitter Sea."

"And bottles of mineral water."

"Yes. Have you tried our Bitter Soda yet? You should. A universal panacea for all the ills afflicting Man."

"Including insomnia?"

"Possibly. I don't drink the muck myself."

"You just make it."

"Yes."

"I often wonder what the vintners make," quoted

Grimes, "one half so precious as the stuff they sell. Or should it be 'buy,' not 'make'? No matter."

"What are you driving at, Commodore?" demanded Clavering.

"I'm not sure myself, Captain. Just thinking out loud. Sort of doodling without pen or paper. And as I can't be getting on with my survey I shall be doing a lot of thinking, just to pass the time. Call me Cassius."

"Cassius?" asked Williams, breaking the silence.

"Yes. He had a lean and hungry look. He thought too much. He was dangerous."

"You'll be able to go on the tours when *Macedon* comes in," said Clavering. "The Painted Badlands. The Valley of the Winds and the Organ Pipes. The Fire Forest. . . ."

"From what I've already learned," said Grimes, "none of them at all suitable sites for a naval base."

"There just aren't any suitable sites. Period."

"Looks as though I was wasting my time coming here, doesn't it?"

"*Sally Ann* will be empty on the run from here to Port Last," said Clavering a little too eagerly. I'll be pleased to give passage to you and Commander Williams and the rest of *Rim Malemute's* officers."

"Thank you, Captain. But we can't accept. Traditions of the Service, and all that. Don't give up the ship. She's our responsibility. I'm afraid we're stuck here until she's repaired."

"I suppose I might tow her back to Port Last for you," suggested Clavering doubtfully.

Grimes went through the motions of considering
this. Then, "Too risky. Deep space towing's a very
specialized job, as Williams, here, will tell you. And
the most awkward part would be getting the *Malemute* off the ground. You've damn all room to play
with in your spaceport at the best of times, and when
your *Sally Ann* lifts off you'll have *Macedon* clutter-
ing up the apron, with mooring wires every which
way. No. Not worth the risk."

"At least," said Clavering, "I shall be having the
pleasure of your company for quite some time." He
was obviously trying to convey the impression that
the prospect was a pleasurable one. He essayed a
smile. "So, gentlemen, make yourselves at home.
This is Liberty Hall. You can spit on the mat and call
the cat a bastard."

The literal minded Williams looked around him,
at the pneumatic furniture, the inflated walls. He
grinned, "If you did have a cat you *would* be calling
him a bastard, or worse, I can just imagine one
racing around in here, digging his claws into everything."

Clavering smiled, genuinely this time. He said,
"This plastic is tougher than it looks. It has to be, as
the devils just refuse to cut their toenails. But it is a
nightmare I have sometimes, the skins of the bubbles
pricked and the whole damn' place just collapsing on
itself like a punctured balloon. But it can't ever
happen."

"Famous last words," said Grimes cheerfully.
"It can't happen here."

"It can't," Clavering told him forcefully.

21

Grimes was far from happy and was wishing, most sincerely, that the Navy had assigned somebody else to work with the Customs in this drug-running investigation. What put him off the job more than anything else was being obliged to accept Clavering's hospitality—it was impossible to live aboard *Rim Malemute* until such time as she was righted. He had insisted that the ex-Captain send the bills for himself and the tug's officers to the Rim Worlds Admiralty, but there were still the rounds of drinks on the house and, with Williams, dining every night at Clavering's table. He was more than ever sure that he was not cut out to be a policeman. But the memories of those three young people—two dead and one with his career ruined—persisted.

He talked matters over with Williams while the two of them paced slowly along the left bank of the Styx. The tug skipper was but a poor substitute for Sonya on such an occasion, but he was the only one in whom Grimes could confide.

He said, "I don't like it, Commander Williams."

"Frankly, Skipper, neither do I. Clavering ain't

all that bad a bastard, an' his wife's a piece of all right, an' here we are, sleepin' in his beds, eatin' his tucker an' slurpin' his grog. An' if all goes well, from our viewpoint, we'll be puttin' him behind bars.''

''Mphm. Not necessarily. His legal status, like that of his world, is rather vague. Even so, the Rim Worlds governments, both over-all and planetary, could make life really hard for him. For example, somebody might decide that Inferno Valley is *the* site for a naval base. But I'm not concerned so much with the legalities. It's the personal freedom angle. If somebody wants to blow his mind, has any government the right to try to stop him?''

''I see what you mean, Skipper. But when that same somebody is in a position of responsibility, like young Pleshoff, he has to be stopped. Or when somebody, like Clavering, is making a very nice profit out of other people's mind-blowing. . . .''

''In most of the Federated worlds it's the governments that make the profits, just as they do from every other so-called vice—liquor, tobacco, gambling. . . . Damn it all, Williams, is Clavering a sinner, or is he just a criminal, only until such time that somebody sees fit to liberalize our laws?''

''I'm not a theologian, Skipper.''

''Neither am I. But both of us, when sailing in command, have been the law *and* the prophets. Both of us have deliberately turned a blind eye to breaches of regulations, whether Company's or Naval.''

''When you're Master under God,'' observed Williams, ''you can do that sort of thing an' get away with it. The trouble now is that we have far too many bastards between us an' the Almighty. It's all very well our hearts fair bleedin' for Clavering—but we have to keep our own jets clear."

"Mphm. All right, then. You suggest that we regard ourselves as policemen, pure and simple."

"I've known a few simple ones," said Williams, "but I've yet to meet one who's pure."

"You know what I mean!" snapped Grimes testily. "Don't try to be funny. Now, we *think* that the dreamy weed is coming in through Eblis, and that it's transhipped from here to Ultimo or wherever in *Ditmar*. Clavering tells me, by the way, that she's still held up. Her yeast vats were condemned. But where was I? Oh, yes. We think that the contraband is shipped from somewhere to Eblis. Through the spaceport? No, I don't think so. Too many people around, even when there's no cruise ship in, who might talk out of turn. Only a dozen of the people here are *Sally Ann* originals; the rest are Rim Worlders. The head waiters, the chef and his assistants, the mechanics in the repair shops. . . . So. So this is a fair hunk of planet, and I'd say that the only man who really knows it is Clavering, and Clavering, by putting the *Malemute* and her boats out of commission, has made sure that we don't get really to know it.

"Our fat friend Billinghurst is due here shortly, in *Macedon*, and he'll be relying on us to lay on transport. And we can't lay it on, and I can't see the Master of *Macedon* lending us one of his boats."

"So we just go on sittin' our big, fat butts doin'

sweet damn' all,'' said Williams. "Suits me, Skipper.''

"It doesn't suit me, Commander Williams. Much as we may dislike it we have a job to do. And as long as we're the ones who're doing it we stand some chance of protecting Clavering from the more serious consequences.''

"That's one way of lookin' at it, Skipper. *And* Mrs. Clavering, of course. Pardon me bein' nosey, but she an' you seem to be gettin' on like a house on fire. Long walks by the river after dinner while Clavering's in his office cookin' his books.''

"If you must know, Commander Williams, she has asked my help, *our* help. She knows that her husband is mixed up in something illegal, but not what it is. She has told me about the prospecting trips that he makes by himself, and about the Carlotti transceiver that he keeps, under lock and key, at his bottling plant by the Bitter Sea.''

"Nothin' wrong with that. When he's out there he has to keep in touch with home.''

"Yes. But an NST transceiver would do for that. You should know by this time that a Carlotti set is only for deep space communications.''

"Just a radio ham,'' suggested Williams. "When he gets tired of hammering the stoppers on to bottles he retires to his den and has a yarn with a cobber on Earth or wherever.''

"Mphm. I doubt it. Anyhow, Mrs. Clavering is far from happy. She'd like to see her husband drop whatever it is he's doing, but she wouldn't like to see him in jail. If we can catch him before that fat ferret

Billinghurst blows in we shall be able to help him to stay free. If Billinghurst gets *his* claws into him, he's a goner.''

"You sure make life complicated, Skipper," complained Williams.

"Life *is* complicated. Period. Now, your work boat. . . ."

"In working order. But if you intend a long trip it'll be so packed with power cells that there'll be room for only one man."

"Good enough. And your engineers, I think, have been passing the time doing what repairs they can to *Malemute*, and have been in and out of Clavering's workshop borrowing tools and such."

"Correct."

"By this time they should be on friendly terms with Clavering's mechanics."

"If they don't know by this time which of the boats it is that Clavering takes out to the Bitter Sea, they should."

"They probably do know."

"I'd like a transponder fitted to Clavering's boat, and the necessary homing gadgetry to your work-boat. I don't know quite how Clavering's boat can be bugged without somebody seeing it done—but, with a little bit of luck, it should be possible. Mphm. Suppose, say, that the inertial drive main rotor has to be carried to the shop so that work can be done on it with one of the lathes. Suppose that everybody— everybody but one man—is clustered around the thing, admiring it. And suppose this one man manages to stick the transponder to the underside of the hull of Clavering's boat when nobody is looking."

"Possible, Skipper, just possible. We already have transponders in stock; they're used quite a lot in salvage work. We've plenty of tubes of wetweld in the stores. An' if Clavering's mechanics know nothin' about the drug racket they'll not be expecting any jiggery pokey from my blokes. Yair. Could be done."

"And how's the repair work on our Carlotti set coming on?"

"Not so good."

"A pity. I'd like to do some monitoring. Just who does Clavering talk to?"

It was some time before the plan could be put into effect. The boat that Clavering usually used for his trips to the Bitter Sea—and for his prospecting trips—was undergoing an extensive and badly needed overhaul. Even without wind-driven abrasives to severely damage the exterior of an atmosphere craft, the air itself was strongly corrosive. Too, most of the work force was engaged on necessary maintenance to make *Sally Ann* thoroughly spaceworthy for her charter trip.

Macedon came in, and aboard her, as a passenger, was Billinghurst. Sub-Inspector Pahvani was with him, and a half dozen other Customs officers. Unlike policemen, Customs officers, when out of uniform, look like anybody else. Billinghurst and his people had no trouble in passing themselves off as ordinary tourists.

22

"Looks like you've been having trouble, Commodore," commented Billinghurst to Grimes as the pair of them stood by the Devil's Stewpot, watching what seemed to be the majority of *Macedon's* passengers wallowing in the murky, bubbling, steaming water. "Sabotage?"

"Accident," replied Grimes. "*Sobraon* was lifting off, and one of her stern vanes snagged one of *Rim Malemute's* mooring wires."

"Accident? You don't really believe that, do you?"

"I've handled ships for long enough, Mr. Billinghurst, to know that accidents do happen."

"All the same, Commodore, it's suspicious," stated Billinghurst.

"How so?" asked Grimes, just to be awkward.

"As I recollect it, the idea was that you were to run a survey of the planet, officially looking for sites for the naval base, and actually looking for places where dreamy weed might be brought in. I don't suppose that you've even started to do that."

"How right you are."

"Meanwhile, you're living in the lap of luxury, and the taxpayer is picking up the tab for your hotel bills."

"The taxpayer forked out for your fare in *Macedon*, and will be picking up the tab for *your* hotel bills."

"That's different."

"How so?"

"Because, Commodore, in matters of this kind I'm a trained investigator. You're not. *You* can't do anything unless you've a ship under you. When *Rim Malemute* was *accidently* knocked out of the picture you were knocked out of it too. I did expect some cooperation from you in the way of transport, but now I'll have to manage as best I can by myself. Don't worry; I've done it before."

"I'm not worrying," said Grimes. He looked with some distaste at an enormously fat, naked man waddling down to the hot pool like a Terran hippopotamus. He asked, "Why don't *you* try the stewpot, Mr. Billinghurst? You could afford to lose some weight."

"Because I've more important things to do, that's why. *I'm* not here on holiday."

"Neither am I, unfortunately."

"So you say."

"So I say. But tell me, just how do you intend to go about things? I realize that I'm just an amateur in these matters, so I'd like to know how a real professional operates."

Billinghurst lapped up the flattery. He said, "In any sort of detective work the human element is, in

310

the final analysis, far more important than all the fancy gadgetry in the laboratories. One informer—voluntary or involuntary—is worth ten scientists. I have chosen to accompany me young, keen officers who are not unattractive to the opposite sex. Sub-Inspector Pahvani you, of course, already know. That is Sub-Inspector Ling just coming out of this absurdly named hot pool."

"Certainly a tasty dollop of trollop," remarked Grimes as the golden-skinned, black-haired, naked girl passed them.

"She is a very fine and capable young woman," said Billinghurst stiffly. "Anyhow, I have young Pahvani and three other men, Miss Ling and two other women. All of them are provided with ample spending money. All of them are to pass themselves off as members of well-to-do families on Thule—they'd have to be well-to-do to afford the fares that TG Clippers charge *and* a quite long holiday here—enjoying a vacation. Captain Clavering has quite a few unattached men and women among his staff here, and my officers have been instructed to . . . to make contacts."

"All over contacts," said Grimes.

"Really, Commodore, you have a low mind."

"Not as low as the mind of the bastard who first thought of using good, honest sex as an espionage tool. But go on."

"Well, I'm hoping that some of Clavering's people become . . . er . . . infatuated with some of my people. And I hope that they—Clavering's people—talk."

"So you can build a case on bedtime stories."

"You put things in the most crude way, Commodore Grimes."

"I'm just a rough and tough spaceman, Mr. Billinghurst. It has been rumored that my rugged exterior hides a heart of gold—but there are times when even I am inclined to doubt that."

"Who's that young man whom Miss Ling is talking to?"

"That's Clavering's chef. Like all good chefs he is always tasting as he cooks. A daily session in the Devil's Stewpot helps him to keep his weight down. He's a Farawegian. He started his career in the kitchen of the Rimrock House at Port Farewell. Mphm. Your Miss Ling is coming back with him for another good sweat session. She must be conscientious. I hope she doesn't lose any weight; she's just right as she is."

"And does this chef *know* anything?"

"He certainly knows cooking. Ah, there's your Mr. Pahvani, getting on with the job. Does he use steel wool on his teeth, by the way? That smile, against his brown skin, is really dazzling. The recipient of the charm that he's turning on is Clavering's head receptionist. She's from Thule, but she prefers it here. Oh, looks like my Commander Williams is making a conquest from among *Macedon's* customers. I must say that I applaud his good taste."

"That," said Billinghurst, "is *my* Miss Dalgety that he's talking to. I'll have to warn her off him."

"Mistakes will happen. After all, you can hardly expect Williams to wear uniform for his daily dip, can you? Any more than you can expect Miss

Dalgety to appear in her Sub-Inspector's finery.''

''You seem to have made *some* enquiries, Commodore,'' admitted Billinghurst reluctantly. ''Perhaps you will oblige me with thumbnail sketches of all Clavering's staff here.''

''All? Devils as well as humans? I'm afraid you're out of luck as far as the devils are concerned. At first I thought I was getting them sorted out by the colour of their scales—and then I found out that this varies from day to day. If you look really hard you can tell which are males and which are females, though.''

''Humans, of course, Commodore.''

''Well,'' began Grimes, ''there's Clavering himself. Spaceman. Hangs on to his Federation citizenship. Still makes an occasional voyage in command of *Sally Ann,* also brings in and takes out ships whose Masters want a pilot.''

''I suppose he was piloting *Sobraon* when she fouled your *Malemute.*''

''As a matter of fact, he was. Wife, Sally Clavering. Tall blonde, very attractive. Ex-purser, and looks after the books of the hotel, the chemical works on the Bitter Sea and the bottling plant. Then there's Larwood, another Federation citizen, Chief Officer of *Sally Ann* and Assistant Port Captain, Assistant Hotel Manager and assistant everything else. Very quiet. Doesn't drink, doesn't smoke, has no time for women. I think there was a marriage once, but it broke up. Ah, here's Mrs. Clavering. Sally, this is Mr. Billinghurst, an old acquaintance from Port Forlorn. Mr. Billinghurst, this is Mrs. Clavering.''

Billinghurst bowed with ponderous dignity. He

said, "I am very pleased to meet you." Then, "This is quite a place you have here. I'd heard so much about it that I just had to come and see it for myself."

"I hope you enjoy your stay, Mr. Billinghurst. We do our best to make our guests feel at home."

Home was never like this, thought Grimes. A slight earth tremor added point to his unspoken comment.

Billinghurst was unshaken. It would have taken a major earthquake to unsettle him. He asked, "Do you have these tremors often, Mrs. Clavering?"

"Quite frequently. You soon get used to them."

"I hope you're right. I hope that I shall. Some people never get used to motion of any kind, and have to take all sorts of drugs to help them to maintain their physical and psychological equilibrium."

She laughed. "We dispense one very good drug for that purpose ourselves, Mr. Billinghurst. You can get it in the bar. It's called alcohol."

"I think I could stand a drink," admitted Billinghurst. "Will you join me, Mrs. Clavering? And you, Commodore?"

"Later, perhaps," she said. She dropped the robe that was all she had been wearing. "I always have my daily hot soak at this time."

Grimes got out of his own dressing gown. "And so do I."

He followed the tall, slim woman into the almost scalding water. They found a place that was out of earshot from the other bathers. She turned to face him, slowly lowered herself until only her head was above the surface. Grimes did likewise, conscious of

314

the stifling heat, of the perspiration pouring down his face.

She said, "I don't like your fat friend, John."

"Neither do I, frankly."

"I never have liked customs officers."

"Customs officers?"

"Don't forget that I was once a spacewoman, a purser. I know the breed. But what were all those not so subtle hints about drugs? Did he expect me to offer him a pipeful of dreamy weed?"

"Perhaps he did," said Grimes. "Perhaps he did."

"Surely you don't think . . .?"

"I wish I didn't."

"But. . . ."

"But the bloody stuff is coming into the Rim Worlds from somewhere, Sally. I know of one young man, an officer in our ships, who got himself emptied out because of it. I know of two other young people who were killed because the container of the weed, dropped from *Ditmar,* was destroyed, by remote control and by explosion, to stop it from falling into Customs' hands. I'm not saying that Ian knew anything about that; I'm sure that he didn't. But—on this world of all worlds!—he should bear in mind the old proverb: He who sups with the devil needs a long spoon."

"You're . . . accusing Ian?"

"The evidence—and what you yourself have told me—point to his being somehow implicated. If he gets out from under now I shall be able, I think and hope, to shield him from the consequences. If he doesn't. . . ."

She looked at him long and earnestly. Then, "Whose side are you on, John?"

"I'm not sure. There are times when I think that stupid laws breed criminals, there are times when I'm not certain that the laws are so stupid. When it comes to things like dreamy weed there's too much hysteria on both sides. It's far easier to handle drugs like alcohol, because nobody has made a religion of them."

"Have you talked to Ian yet, as I asked you to?"

"I've tried once or twice, but he's very hard to pin down."

"Don't I know it! But I think he realizes that the game's up and that he's let whoever has been bringing the stuff in that the trade is finished."

"He hasn't been able to get out to his bottling plant where he has his private transceiver. His air boat is still under repair, and it would take too long by road."

Sure said, "Surely the Port Captain is allowed to play around with the Carlotti equipment in the control tower in his own spaceport."

"Oh, well," said Grimes, "I'll shed no tears if it turns out that I've come here for nothing."

23

Seeing a planet as a tourist is not the same as running your own survey, but it is better than not seeing a planet at all. *Macedon,* with all her experience-hungry passengers, was in, and the three large atmosphere fliers, the aircoaches, were now completely overhauled and ready for service.

Billinghurst sneered at Grimes and Williams, saying that they were having a glorious holiday at public expense. He preferred to stay in Inferno Valley, keeping his eyes and his ears open. The only one of his officers to go on the tours was Denise Dalgety—but not so that she could continue to turn her considerable charm on to Williams. She had transferred her attentions to Larwood, who was in charge of the sightseeing expeditions. Grimes felt sorry for the dark, morose assistant manager. He would have liked to have warned him. More and more it was becoming obvious that he appreciated the company of the plump redhead who, ever more frequently, was able to coax an occasional smile from him. Sooner or later there would have to be a rude awakening.

317

The first trip was to the Painted Badlands. Grimes and Williams rode in the leading air coach, the command vehicle, which was piloted by Larwood. They had been given seats right forward, on the starboard side, immediately abaft the pilot. In the corresponding seats to port were an elderly Terran businessman and his wife, both looking slightly ludicrous in the heavy duty one piece suits, as much metal as fibre, that were mandatory wear. There was a single seat to port of that occupied by Larwood; in this, of course, sat Denise Dalgety. In any form of transport whatsoever rank hath its privileges. She, apart from Williams, was the only young passenger in the coach. Her companions had said, rather too loudly, at the bar the previous night, that they didn't want to be herded around with a lot of old fossils.)

Dawn was just coming in when the three coaches lifted from the landing field close by the hotel. Their inertial drives hammering erratically, they climbed slowly, drifting a little to the west so that the fantastic bubble structure, multihued and luminescent, lay beneath them. Grimes permitted himself to wonder what would be the effect of a few handfuls of heavy steel darts dropped from the aircraft.

Slowly they climbed, hugging the north wall of the canyon which, in this light, was blue rather than red, splotched with opalescent patches where grew the phosphorescent lichen and fungi. Slowly they climbed, and with every meter of altitude they gained the orange ribbon of sky directly above them widened. ''Aero-space Control to Painted Badlands Tour,'' came a matter-of-fact voice from the transceiver. "There's as much of a lull as you're likely to get. Keep clear of the Devil's Phallus. There's turbulence. Over."

"PB Tour to Aero-Space Control. Roger. Over."

Grimes grinned to himself. This, he knew, was all part of the window dressing.

Larwood said into his microphone, "Make sure your seat belts are fastened, folks. We may get a few bumps when we clear the canyon rim."

There were a few bumps, but very minor ones. The coaches were lifting under maximum thrust now, and below them was Inferno Valley, a deep, dark slash in the face of the planet. To the south towered the Erebus Alps, peak after conical peak, from each of which a pillar of flame—shot smoke rose almost vertically. Dim in the distance were the Devil's Torches, volcanoes even more spectacularly active than those of the Alps. And beyond those? The Infernal Beacons? It was hard to be sure. Already the early morning clarity of the atmosphere was becoming befouled.

The note of the inertial drive changed as Larwood brought his coach around to a northerly heading. He announced, "If you look hard, folks, you'll see the Bitter Sea out to port, on our left. We shall be stopping there overnight on our way back. Most of the day we shall be spending in the Painted Badlands, of course."

"Pilot!" This was an old lady well back in the coach. "We've come all this way and you've shown us practically nothing of the Erebus Alps and the other ranges."

"I may wear wings on my uniform, madam," Larwood told her, "but they aren't bat's wings. A devil, one of those mythological devils out of the mythological hell, might survive there, but we certainly shouldn't. Updraughts, downdraughts, red hot boulders hurtling through the air—you name it, the Erebus Alps and the other ranges have got it. But I promise you that the Painted Badlands will be an experience none of you will ever forget. Now, all of you, you can either look astern, behind you, or at the stern view screen that is in front of every seat. I've just switched it on. The screen might be clearer. You will realize the sort of muck and rubbish we should have to fly through. The wind's just starting to rise."

Muck and rubbish, thought Grimes, peering into the screen that he shared with Williams. *A good description.* The pillars of fiery smoke from the multitudinous craters were leaning towers now, blown ever further and further from the vertical until they approached the horizontal. The sharp outlines of the peaks were blurred, were obscured by the wind-driven fumes and dust. Overhead the sky was no longer orange but a glowing yellow across which scudded the low black clouds. And below, the whirling flurries of red dust were blotting out all landmarks. Then, through some meteorological freak, the air ahead of them cleared and, brooding sullenly over the red plain, the Great Smokies appeared, almost black against the yellow sky, belching volumes of white steam and dark brown smoke.

"But you're flying over *them*, Pilot!" complained the old lady accusingly.

"Not over, madam. Through. Just fine in our

starboard bow, a little to the right of dead ahead, you'll see the entrance to Dante's Pass. Also, if you will look at the smoke from the volcanoes, you will see that the wind is nowhere near as bad as it is to the south'ard. The Smokies are in the lee of the highest part of Satan's Barrier.''

"But these mountains are only *smoking*," muttered the old lady.

"If we'd only known," whispered Williams to Grimes, "we could have brought along a couple of nuclear devices just to keep the old dear happy."

"Mphm. Smoke or flame—this is a good place for a holiday, but I wouldn't want to live here."

"Don't mention holidays, Skipper. Glamorpuss up ahead might hear you."

Denise Dalgety turned in her seat, smiled sweetly at Williams. "I'm enjoying *my* holiday," she said.

"What was all that about, Denise?" asked Larwood.

"Nothing much, Ron. Nothing much. Just something that Commander Williams said."

"Oh," grunted Larwood. Then, into the microphone again, "Coming up to Dante's Pass now, folks. To port, Mount Dante. To starboard, Mount Beatrice. Looks like Dante's a heavy smoker still, but Beatrice seems to have kicked the habit. Ha, ha."

Ha, ha, thought Grimes. *I'm rolling in the aisle in a paroxysm of uncontrollable mirth.*

But his irritation faded as he stared out at the spectacular scenery. The coach had dropped to an altitude well below that of the peaks, seemed to be barely skimming the numerous minor craters that pocked the valley floor. Smoke was issuing from almost all of them—in some cases a trickle, in others as a billowing cloud. And all up the steep, terraced side of Dante were similar small craters, most of them active. The slopes of Mount Beatrice were also pockmarked but, for some reason, only an occasional wisp of vapor was evident.

"You could do better, Skipper," whispered Williams.

Grimes, who had brought out his pipe and was about to fill it, changed his mind and put the thing back in his pocket.

On they flew, and on, the three coaches in line ahead, the Great Smokies to either side of their course and at last falling astern. On they flew, and the smoldering mountain range dropped astern, and the foothills, each of which was a volcano. Smoke eddied about them, restricting visibility, often blotting out the view of the tortured landscape below them. Turbulence buffeted them, and once the coaches had to make a wide alteration of course to avoid a huge red tornado.

Desert was below them at last—huge dunes the faces of which displayed all colors from brown through red to a yellow that was almost white, with streaks of gray and silver and blue. Beyond the dunes was a region where great rock pillars towered like the ruins of some ancient devastated city, sculpted by wind and sand into fantastic shapes, glowing with raw color.

"The Painted Badlands," announced Larwood unnecessarily. "The wind's from the west still, so it's safe to land."

"What if the wind was from the east?" asked the old lady.

"Then, madam, we shouldn't have the protection of Satan's Barrier. There'd be a sandstorm that'd strip us to our bare bones. You can see what wind and sand have done to those rocks down there."

The irregular hammering of the inertial drive became less insistent. The coach slowed, began losing altitude. It dropped at last to coarse red sand in what could have been a city square, a clear space with the eroded monoliths all about it. The second vehicle landed in a flurry of ruddy dust, then the third.

"Welcome to Dis," said Larwood. "You may disembark for sight-seeing. Respirators will be worn; I wouldn't say that the atmosphere's actually poisonous, but too much of it wouldn't do your eyes, throats or lungs any good. You will all stay with me and not go wandering off by yourselves. You may pick up souvenirs—pretty pebbles and the like—within reason, but I warn you that this wagon doesn't develop enough thrust to carry home one of the monoliths. Ha, ha."

One by one the passengers passed out through the airlock, jumped or clambered down to the windswept sand.

"If it wasn't for the easterlies," said Williams to Grimes, his voice muffled by his breathing mask, "this'd be a good spot for a Base."

"At least," said Grimes, "we shall be able to write some sort of report on this base business now. Just in case somebody actually asks for it."

24

It was a long day, and a tiring one. A heavy protective suit complete with respirator is not the most comfortable wear for sight-seeing, and Larwood was determined that they should see everything.

They looked at the Venus de Milo—which, if one used one's imagination, just could have been a giant statue of a woman, carved from black basalt, minus her arms. Their guide made the inevitable joke about the consequences of fingernail biting. They saw the Leaning Tower of Pisa. It did lean, but there all resemblance ceased. They saw the Sphinx, which was not too unlike a great, crouching cat if looked at from the right angle, and the Great Pyramid. They returned to the comparative luxury of the coaches for a sandwich meal and very welcome cold drinks. After lunch a short flight took them away from the so-called City Square of Dis to another part of the Badlands. Here they saw the Colossus of Eblis, which vaguely resembled a man standing arrogantly with his legs apart, the Thinker—Larwood, of course, had to say that a huge stone toilet roll was being carved to hang alongside the seated, brooding figure—Mount Olga and Ayers Rock. Grimes made himself unpopular by saying that the originals of these last two named gained greatly in majesty by being situated in a vast empty desert with no surrounding clutter to distract attention from them.

They saw the Devil's Launching Pad, a low plateau surmounted by a remarkably regular row of what, from a distance, could have been archaic space rockets. They saw the Dinosaurs, and St. Paul's Cathedral, and St. Bazil's Cathedral, and the Rainbow Bridge. They saw. . . . But it was all too much, much too much, at the finish. They stumbled through the surrealistic landscape, the rockscape, with its great contorted masses of garishly coloured stone, behind their guides. Even Larwood was running short of witticisms, although he did say that it just required one good crash to make the Lorelei look happy.

Tired, perspiring in their suits and behind their masks, they stumbled back into the coaches, gratefully loosening clothing and removing respirators. The irregular blotch of brightness in the yellow sky that was the sun was low in the west when they lifted, but there was daylight enough for the coaches to negotiate Dante's Pass without trouble, and Mount Beatrice honoured them with a salute, a huge, spectacular smoke ring, as they flew past. The sun was not yet down when they approached the western shores of the Bitter Sea and the white buildings of the bottling plant, on the bank of the River of Tears, stood out against the dusky red of the desert like a

325

handful of white pebbles dropped there. As they
approached they could see that these were of the by
now familiar bubble construction—although, Larwood told them, the skins were centimeters instead
of mere millimeters thick, and had frequently to be
renewed.

He announced, on his public address system,
"We shall be staying here overnight, folks. One
dome has been fitted out as a dormitory for tourists,
and the one adjoining as a mess hall. At dark floodlights will be turned on so that you may all enjoy a
swim in the Bitter Sea. You will have time for
another one in the morning, before we leave for
Inferno Valley. Oh, before I forget, there are fresh
water showering facilities at the Bottling Plant. I
advise you all to take a shower after swimming in the
Bitter Sea."

"Swimming, the man said," complained Grimes,
his voice muffled by the respirator that, now, was all
that he was wearing.

"Walkin' on the water's just the thing for a high
an' mighty Commodore," laughed Williams.

"But not for a mere Commander, like you."

"I wonder if one could really walk on it," murmured Williams. He managed a sitting posture and
then overbalanced, finishing up flat on his back. He
said, "Any bastard tryin' to commit suicide in this
soup'd die o' frustration."

"Mphm." Grimes managed a kind of squat and
looked around him. The other passengers were enjoying themselves, splashing and squealing in the
harsh glare of the floodlights. But the one he was

looking for—the only one who would have been worth looking at—was not there. Neither was Larwood, although the other two coach pilots were disporting themselves with their charges.

"Mphm," grunted Grimes again. So Billinghurst's pet blonde spy was earning her keep whilst he and Williams were having a good time. But perhaps she was having a good time too.

"Lookin' for Denise?" asked Williams.

"As a matter of fact, yes."

"She went off with that frosty-faced sidekick o' Clavering's just before we all got undressed for our dip. I suppose he's showin' her his etchings. Unless I get outer this hellbroth soon I'll be able to show all the girls my itchings!"

"Yes, it does seem to be mildly corrosive. I'd hate to swallow any. Coming out?"

"Too bleedin' right, Skipper. When I want a swim I have a swim, when I want a walk I have a walk. What we're doin' now is just a compromise."

Clumsily the two men splashed ashore. Once they were through the airlock of the bottling plant they removed their respirators, handing them to attentive attendant devils. They followed one of the natives to the showers, where others of his kind were scampering around in the clouds of steam armed with long-handled brushes, enthusiastically scrubbing down the naked humans. The red lighting of the place made it all look like a scene from a mythological Inferno—and, muttered Grimes, some of the tourists looked like refugees from the canvases of Hieronymus Bosch.

After their showers—hot water and detergent to

remove the salty scum, cold water for refreshment—the two men got into clean coveralls provided by the management, collected personal belongings from their lockers in the change room, then strolled into the dormitory. There was no sign of either Denise Dalgety or of Larwood. They walked into the mess hall, where a few people were sitting over cold drinks. The girl and Clavering's assistant were not there either.

Grimes wasn't worried—what Billinghurst's officers did with themselves, or had done to them, was none of his concern—but he was curious. Perhaps "curious" is not quite the right word. He had the feeling that the girl was finding out something and would have liked very much to know what it was. Perhaps pride was involved. He could imagine Billinghurst telling his story to an appreciative audience: "There was the famous Commodore Grimes, and all that *he* did was to get his ship wrecked and then, with nothing at all that *he* could do, have one helluva good time like a tourist, at the taxpayer's expense. One of *my* Sub-Inspectors, a girl at that, did much better than *he* did."

"Denise Dalgety, the Beautiful Blonde Spy," muttered Williams.

"Jealous, Commander?"

"My oath, yes. I still haven't forgiven that bastard Billinghurst for calling her off me. He ruined the beginnings of what promised to be a beautiful friendship. I wonder where he's taken her? Larwood, I mean."

"Clavering has an office here. Presumably his second-in-command has a set of keys to it."

"An' now he's chasin' her round the water cooler
. . . or she's chasin' him round the water cooler."

"The chasing part," said Grimes, "must be well
over."

"Some people are slow starters. All right, then.
He's sittin' there, with a silly smile on his face, while
she photographs the plans of the fortifications with
the miniature camera hidden in one of her clips,
which are the only things she's wearin' at the moment. There's a recorder in the other clip."

"Try to be serious, Williams."

"What about, Skipper? It'd be a lot easier for me
if I knew which side you were on. Are you pro- or
anti-smuggler? I know damn well that you're anti-
Billinghurst—but who's not? Ever since we've been
on this bloody job you've been obscuring the issue
with a fog of moral principles. And we aren't concerned with the moral side of it, only with the legal
side."

"And that," Grimes told him, "is even more
obscure. Whose laws apply on this planet—the laws
of the Confederacy or the laws that Clavering makes
up as he goes along? The Confederacy, don't forget,
didn't want Eblis. Clavering saw its possibilities."

"And so what? As planetary ruler he pays his
taxes to the Confederacy rather than to the
Federation—because that way he pays less. But, by
so doing, he has admitted Confederate jurisdiction."

"Here she comes," said Grimes in a low voice.

Here she came. She saw Grimes and Williams,
walked to the table where they were seated. An
attentive devil clattered up to take her drink order.
She waved the native away.

329

"Commodore," she said, smiling sweetly, "I understand that you're attached to this investigation as an astronautical expert."

"Mphm. I suppose so."

"Ron showed me round the bottling plant. He said that I should see more if I had his undivided attention, that it would be better than going on the conducted tour of inspection later this evening."

"Mphm."

"It wasn't very interesting really. Just machines doing things, washing bottles, filling bottles, sealing bottles. . . ."

"Mphm."

"And then he took me into the office."

Grimes, looking at Williams' face, had trouble in keeping his own straight.

"I'm not very well up on ships' instruments. Usually I'm concerned with passengers' baggage. Tell me, Commodore, that radio with an antenna like a Mobius Strip, formed as a long ellipse, universally mounted, is a Carlotti transceiver, isn't it?"

"It is." (But he knew already that there was one in the bottling plant.)

"And it's never used for short range signalings? Only ship to ship, ship to planet, planet to ship, planet to planet?"

"As a general rule."

"A message came through while we were. . . ." She blushed. "Well, a message came through. Ron said that I'd have to leave the office, as it was probably Captain Clavering calling about some important business and, even though he trusted me, some matters regarding the bottling of the River of Tears water were a commercial secret. Luckily I'd taken my ear clips off, and left them behind when I went out. And then, after. . . ." She blushed again. "And then after I left Ron—he let me back inside when whoever it was had finished sending—I played it back when I went into the toilet."

She detached the ornament of interlocking golden rings from her right ear, put it on the table. She said, "I have it set for the lowest volume. You'll have to pretend to be looking at it closely. Press the spring clip."

"An interesting piece of jewelry," commented Grimes, picking it up. "Very fine workmanship."

He heard, "Damn! The Old Man's calling from Inferno Valley!" (Presumably earlier conversation had been censored by one of those involved.) "Let him call." "But darling, it could be important," "Answer it then, and get it over." "Denise, it's not that I don't trust you, but it could be something confidential." "All right then, I'll go out into the main office. Give me time to put something on." "There's no need, all the doors are locked." "Do you think more of your boss than you do of me?" "Please, Denise, just leave me and let me answer this call." "All right, all right. I bet Billy Williams wouldn't drop me like a hot cake and come a-running if Commodore Grimes whistled for him!" A hissing silence, then, "SB three calling IC. Anyone there? I repeat, anyone there?" The voice was oddly familiar. "IC answering SB three. This is RL receiving you." "I've a shipment for you, IC. Will advise later when. Presumably usual place. Over." "But, SB three, the heat's on." "You'll want this shipment for the Convention, won't you? Over, and most definitely out." Silence, then Ron Larwood's voice again, presumably on a normal telephone. "That you, Sally? Can I get hold of the Captain? I'll call later then. No, no trouble with the tour. Very well behaved bunch of customers. See you tomorrow. Goodnight."

And that was all. There are more secrets than commercial ones.

25

Before they could all sit down to their evening meal there was the conducted tour of the bottling plant—all very boring unless one happened to be an engineer. Larwood pointed out with pride the way in which the machinery was mounted on floating platforms so that it would suffer no damage, and even go on functioning, in the event of an earth tremor. There were free samplings of the mineral-rich water, from which Grimes and Williams abstained. What had happened during their first night on Eblis had put them off the stuff.

Grimes, more out of spite than from any desire to know, asked, "And what's behind that door, Mr. Larwood?"

"Just the office, Commodore Grimes. Nothing of any interest whatsoever."

"I'd rather like to see it, Mr. Larwood. As I spend most of my days behind an office desk I might get some ideas as to how to make myself more comfortable. If your office is like the plant it'll be up to the minute."

"I'm sorry, Commodore. Only Captain Clavering

has the keys. In any case, there's nothing at all to see.''

"Some other day, perhaps?" said Grimes vaguely.

"Yes, Commodore. Some other day."

And then they were all sitting down at the tables in the mess hall, and the devils were bringing in steaming platters of food and bottles of cold wine, and everybody was tucking in to the bouillabaisse made from various denizens of the Bitter Sea as though none of them had eaten for at least a week. Even Williams enjoyed it, leaving nothing in his bowl but empty shells and cracked claws. Denise Dalgety, who was at the next table, was eating with a very good appetite, but Larwood was off his feed.

It was bedtime then, and the tourists retired to the dormitory. The air mattresses were very comfortable, and even the chorus of snores from all around him could not keep the Commodore awake. He was vaguely conscious of a slight earth tremor just before he dropped off, but it did not worry him.

Music over the public address system woke the tourists. Most of them went out for a last swim in the Bitter Sea, but Grimes and Williams did not. Apart from anything else there was privacy for conversation in the shower room.

"I wonder just who SB three is," said Grimes. "That voice sounded familiar. I've heard it before, but a very long time ago. It made quite an impression on me."

"One o' the Australoid accents, Skipper," said Williams.

"Pots and kettles, Commander. Pots and kettles. But it hadn't got that peculiar Rim Worlds twang, like yours."

"Austral?" suggested Williams doubtfully.

"Mphm. Yes. Could be. And those initials, SB, ring some kind of bell too. IC is obviously Ian Clavering, and RL is Ron Larwood. Do we know anybody who has SB for initials?"

"*I* don't, Skipper, 'cept for a shelia back on Lorn called Susan Bartram. It couldn't have been her."

"How do you know? In this sort of business all sorts of odd people may be implicated."

"It wasn't a woman's voice," began Williams, then realized that Grimes was not entirely serious.

"Yes, as you say, Commander, it was a man's voice. But whose?"

"There're one helluva lot o' men in this Galaxy—an' you, in your lifetime, have met at least your fair share of 'em."

"Too right."

And then the first of the bathers came in from the Bitter Sea, and the attendant devils got busy with detergent and long-handled brushes, and there was no more opportunity for conversation.

After a good breakfast the tourists got back into the coaches. The first pallor of dawn was showing in the eastern sky, with the black plumed Great Smokies in silhouette against the yellow luminosity, when the vehicles lifted. To the south'ard the low clouds reflected the glare from the Erebus Alps and the Devil's Torches. The wind had yet to rise, although the Bitter Sea was well enough in the lee of

Satan's Barrier to be shielded from the full fury of the westerlies.

Larwood and the other two pilots wasted no time. Was he in a hurry, wondered Grimes, because he wanted to report that odd deep space radio call to Clavering, or because he wanted to get back to Inferno Valley while the dawn lull lasted? But he must have called Clavering again last night, after he had got rid of Denise Dalgety. And Clavering was to lift off at sunset in *Sally Ann* on his charter voyage, so Larwood must have made sure of getting in touch with him as soon as possible.

The sun came up—and there, ahead, was the dark gash in the ochre desert that was Inferno Valley. From its eastern end white steam, from the Devil's Stewpot, was lazily rising, curling in wreaths about the Devil's Phallus. *One thing about this world,* thought Grimes, *there's no need to go the trouble and expense of putting up wind socks.*

Larwood started to lose altitude as the coaches approached the western end of the valley, dropped below the lips of the canyon as soon as possible, skimmed over the placid waters of the Styx at reduced speed, almost brushing the upper branches of the ghost gums along its banks.

He grounded just in front of the main entrance to the Lucifer Arms, said into his public address microphone, "Well, that's all, folks. Thank you for your company and cooperation."

Williams looked at the back of Denise Dalgety's blonde head and whispered, "She and the Mate

"Would cooperate

"Upon the office table."

"There's probably a settee in there," said Grimes, taking a malicious pleasure in seeing the girl's ears redden.

"All ashore what's going ashore!" said Larwood with spurious heartiness. "This is the end of the penny section!"

Clavering, Grimes noticed, was waiting just inside the hotel entrance. He looked impatient. Grimes could not see Larwood's face, but the back of his neck looked impatient too. Slowly, clumsily, the tourists extricated themselves from the coach. Grimes and Williams politely held back to let Denise Dalgety out first. She said sweetly, "After you, Commodore," but Larwood seemed anxious to be rid of her.

At last they were all out, standing in gossiping groups on the firm red sand. Larwood, his responsibilities at an end, went straight to Clavering. The two men exchanged a few brief words and then went into the hotel, brushing past Billinghurst, who was on his way out. Denise Dalgety walked swiftly towards the fat Customs chief to make her report.

"Nobody loves *us*, Commander," said Grimes sadly.

"Is it surprising, Skipper?" countered Williams.

26

Grimes managed to have a few words in private with Clavering before his departure for Ultimo. It was natural enough that he should wish to have a look over *Sally Ann,* and that vessel's Master could not very well refuse his request.

When they were in the old liner's control room Grimes said seriously, "I'm warning you, Captain."

"What about, Commodore?" Clavering's voice was altogether too innocent.

"You know."

"All right. So I know. So what?"

"Try to get out of this mess that you've gotten into, man. Tell whoever's behind the racket that he'll have to find some other way of bringing the stuff in. The risk, for you, just isn't worth it. You've built up a very nice little business here—a not so little business, rather. How long will it last if the Confederacy gets really hostile?"

Clavering said stiffly, "For your information I *am* pulling out." His face worked strangely. "Also for your information—I knew Inga Telfer. I . . . I

knew her well. I don't need to tell you, Commodore
Grimes, that the owner and manager of a holiday
resort has even better opportunities than a passenger
ship officer. Did you see any of Inga's work?
There's a lot of Eblis in it; she was always saying that
this planet is a painter's paradise. Eblis and dreamy
weed, and all splashed down on canvas. When I
heard of her death I was . . . shocked. I want
nothing more to do with the traffic that killed her.
Satisfied?''

''Mphm. What about the consignment that's on
the way?''

''What consignment?'' countered Clavering.

''I just assumed that there would be one,'' said
Grimes. He could not say more for fear of blowing
Denise Dalgety's cover.

''Assume all you like,'' said Clavering.

And then his Chief Officer—not Larwood, who
would be staying behind to run things in his captain's
absence—came in to report that he had completed
the pre-liftoff inspection.

''Thank you, Mr. Tilden,'' said Clavering. ''And
now, if you'll excuse me, Commodore, I have to
start thinking about getting this old lady upstairs.
Mr. Tilden will show you to the after airlock.''

''This way, sir,'' said the Mate.

''A pleasant voyage, Captain,'' said Grimes.

''Thank you. Enjoy your stay on Eblis, Commodore.''

''I'll do just that,'' promised Grimes.

Not so very long later he stood with Billinghurst

and Williams, a little apart from *Macedon's* passengers, and watched *Sally Ann* lifting off. The big ship climbed slowly and, it seemed, laboriously—although this impression may have been due to the way in which the irregular hammering of her inertial drive was echoed back from the red basalt cliffs of the canyon walls. Slowly she climbed, clambering up towards the strip of darkling yellow sky far overhead, her far from inconsiderable bulk dwarfed by the towering monolith of the Devil's Phallus. Slowly she climbed at first, then faster and faster, hurrying to get clear of the atmosphere during the sunset lull.

Abruptly Billinghurst asked, "Did *you* find anything out, Commodore?"

"Eh? What?"

"I asked," repeated the fat man patiently, "if *you* found anything out?"

"I don't wear ear clips," said Grimes.

"Ha, ha. Very funny. But, talking of electronic gadgetry, it's a bloody pity you haven't got *your* Carlotti receiver repaired yet."

"Why?"

"Do I have to spell it out? Because then we could monitor all incoming and outgoing signals."

"Not necessarily," Grimes told him. "This mysterious SB Three could be sending on a very tight beam, aimed directly at the bottling plant. I didn't get a look at the transreceiver there myself, but probably it's designed for tight beam transmission."

"Not that it makes any difference," said Billinghurst, "since *you* can't do anything about it, anyhow."

I've got Clavering's word that he's pulling out,

thought Grimes. *For what it's worth.* . . . How many times have men engaged in illegal activities said, "Just one more time?" Too many. Far too many. And was Clavering already using his ship's Carlotti equipment to establish communication with SB Three? All too likely.

"I don't suppose anything will happen until Clavering gets back," said Billinghurst.

"If then," said Grimes.

"Are you helping me or not, Commodore?"

"I was merely expressing an opinion. For your information, Mr. Billinghurst, as you should have gathered from the conversation your Miss Dalgety recorded, everybody on this planet knows who you are and what you're here for, and they suspect that my story about the projected naval base is just a blind. The way in which *Ditmar's* been held up at Port Last stinks to high heaven. It's obvious, as Larwood said, that the heat's on."

"When the heat is on, Commodore, people get panicky and make silly mistakes."

"Some people do, but not all."

"These ones will," said Billinghurst flatly, and waddled off.

"The old bastard really loves you, Skipper," commented Williams.

"Doesn't he? Damn it all, Commander, I rather envy him. To be in a job where there's no question of rights or wrongs or personal freedoms, just what's legal and what's illegal. . . ."

"Remember Pleshoff and Fellini and Inga Telfer."

"Pleshoff's a young idiot, and unlucky to boot.

Fellini and the girl were killed by H.E., not by dreamy weed. Too, we're just assuming that the charge in the drop container was detonated deliberately. Don't forget that it was under fire from laser and projectile weapons.''

''If you were takin' a more active part, Skipper, you'd be far happier. You wouldn't be carryin' on as if yer name was Hamlet, not Grimes.''

''Perhaps you're right. If only we had the *Malemute* in running order. . . .''

''But we haven't. But we still have the work boat, and that transponder is still stuck to Captain Clavering's pet atmosphere flier.''

''For all the good it is,'' said Grimes.

27

It seemed safe to assume that nothing would happen until Clavering's return from Ultimo, if then. Billinghurst condescended to explain to Grimes the part that the Commodore would have to play should the mysterious SB Three land on Eblis to discharge a consignment of dreamy weed.

"We have to bear in mind," he said, "that we're surrounded by legal complications. We can't touch Clavering—or, if we do, his legal eagles are going to raise a scream that'll be heard from here to the Magellanic Clouds. Given time, no doubt, we could nail something on him. But what? No matter. SB Three, however, is most definitely a lawbreaker. He—or she, or it, for all I know—is landing on one of the Rim Worlds without going through the formalities of obtaining an Inward Clearance. He and his ship are liable to arrest. I have the legal power to make such an arrest, of course—but usually, in such cases, the Navy is called upon to seize on behalf of the Customs Department. You, even with the small handful of *Rim Malemute's* officers at your disposal, will be able to put a prize crew aboard the seized vessel and take her to Port Last.''

"I suppose so,'' admitted Grimes. "I'd be happier if I had the *Malemute* at my disposal as well as her officers, though. I had the little bitch fitted with a good set of teeth, and now she won't be able to show them, let alone use them.''

"This isn't a naval action, Commodore. This is merely the seizure of a smuggler.''

"Mphm. Some quite respectable merchant vessels are armed like young cruisers. I shouldn't be at all surprised if SB Three, if he shows up, packs an even heavier wallop.''

"When SB Three shows up,'' said Billinghurst firmly, "we will arrest him.''

"And meanwhile?''

"My people will continue to cultivate the friendships they have made. So far the only one to have got results is Miss Dalgety. As you know. It isn't up to me to give you orders, Commodore, but perhaps if you continued making your sightseeing tours you might learn something.''

"Thank you,'' said Grimes, with mock humility.

So he saw the Valley of the Winds and listened to the Devil's Organ—which, he said, reminded him of the lowing of a sick cow. He visited the Burning Pits, and he and Williams amused themselves by imagining Billinghurst being reduced to a puddle of grease at the bottom of the Wishing Well, into which they threw coins to watch them become blobs of molten silver in seconds. They were flown over the Fire Forests on a day when conditions were suitable, and applauded with the rest of the tourists when Larwood solemnly named a new volcano Mount Denise, swooping low to drop a bottle of champagne (he always carried a few on this trip for such occasions) into the bubbling crater.

They dined and danced in the Lucifer Arms, they perspired in the Devil's Stewpot and even, eventually, got into the habit of running straight from its almost boiling waters into the artificially cooled Purgatorial Pool. They spent evenings in the Gambling Hell and soon learned to avoid the One Fingered Bandits so as to make their money last longer at the TriDi Roulette tanks. Insofar as the smuggling was concerned they saw nothing, heard nothing, learned nothing. As far as they could gather Denise Dalgety, although enjoying herself even more than they were, had learned nothing further, and neither had the other undercover Customs agents.

Finally *Macedon* departed on the next leg of her Galactic cruise and the hotel was almost empty again, the only guests being Billinghurst and his people and *Rim Malemute's* crew. Larwood busied himself with the overhaul of the tourist coaches and Denise Dalgety, left to her own devices and not liking it, took up with Williams. Grimes spent much of his spare time in the company of Sally Clavering. Billinghurst sat around and sulked.

Then, with the ship *Sally Ann* on her way back from Port Last, there was an outbreak of fresh activity. The main lounge was converted into a dining room, and the vast, domed dining hall was stripped of its furniture—an easy job, since it had merely to

345

be deflated and stowed—and hung with sombre black drapes.

"I don't like it, John," confessed Sally Clavering to Grimes. "But this is the way *they* want it, and *they're* paying."

"*They,* I take it, being the Church of the Gateway."

"Yes. They must be going to hold services in here. But . . . all this black. No crucifixes, or stars and crescents . . . not even a Crux Ansata."

"Not even an alarm clock," said Grimes. "I was on Darsha once, and went to a service in the famous Tower of Darkness. The clock is running down, and all that. Made quite an impression on me. I suppose Entropy is as good a god as any, although not to my taste."

"Do you know anything about these Gateway people, John?"

"Hardly a thing, Sally. It's a new cult that's sprung up on Ultimo, quite recently." *And,* he thought, *dreamy weed's mixed up in it somehow. The hallucinogens have been part and parcel of quite a few freak religions.*

She said, "I don't think I shall like them. I wish Ian hadn't agreed to let them hold their convention here. But they're paying well."

"Thirty pieces of silver?" asked Grimes.

She snapped, "That's not funny."

"I'm sorry, Sally. But . . . I could be wrong, I probably am, but it often seems to me that religion has betrayed Man more times than it has led him upwards."

"I don't agree."

"You don't have to. Even so, what Marx said seems, to me, to have validity. Religion is the opium of the people." *And opium is the religion of some people.*

"Marx . . . there's a false prophet for you."

"Not altogether false." He laughed. "I'm a spaceman and you're an ex-spacewoman, and the pair of us should know better than to discuss two of the subjects that are taboo in space—religion and politics."

She said, "We're not aboard ship now."

"We might as well be. Just a handful of men and women living in one little valley on a hostile planet. . . ."

"You'll be serving out the rifles and the revolvers next, to fight off the hostile natives."

"Are they restless tonight?" *I know that I am,* he thought, *I can't help feeling that Clavering's going to do one last piece of drug running–and, as far as he's concerned, it will be quite legal. But SB Three will be on the wrong side of the fence as far as the law's concerned.*

He excused himself as soon as he decently could, went to find Billinghurst, told him what he suspected. The Customs officer was scornful. He said, "You only see the obvious, Grimes, when your nose is rubbed in it. The convention was mentioned in that Carlotti call recorded by Miss Dalgety. You and your officers had better be on their toes when Clavering gets back with his shipload of cranks. I've already warned my people."

"I don't think, somehow," said Grimes, "that SB Three will be landing in Inferno Valley."

"Are you sure you can't get your bloody ship fixed in time?" demanded Billinghurst.

"Quite sure," Grimes told him.

28

Sally Ann came in from Ultimo, dropping down through the morning twilight, the dawn lull, the eddying streamers of white mist rising sluggishly from the Devil's Stewpot. *Sally Ann* came in, and all Clavering's staff, as well as the guests at his hotel, were out to watch the berthing. The big ship settled gently to her pad just beyond the crippled *Malemute*. Almost immediately the mooring crew of devils, under Larwood's direction, swarmed over her, shackling on and setting up the wire stays. Only when this job was completed did the last mutterings of the liner's inertial drive fade into silence. Then, up and along her towering hull, airlock doors opened and ramps were extruded.

Disembarkation at a port like Inferno Valley—as Grimes took pleasure in pointing out to Billinghurst—was not a lengthy procedure. There were no Port Health, Immigration, or Customs officials to slow things up. Within seconds the first passengers were trooping ashore.

Grimes looked at them curiously. They were like—yet markedly unlike—the spheres with whom he had rolled at Port Last. The women's heads were shaven, the men all had long hair and beards. But most of them belonged to a different age group, were older, and wore long dark robes instead of form revealing clothing.

Larwood came to greet the first group down the ramp. He saluted the man who seemed to be in charge. He asked courteously, "Are you the . . . er . . . leader, sir?"

The tall, gray-haired and gray-bearded man replied, "Yes, my son. I am the Guru William. Is all prepared for us?"

"All is prepared, Your . . . Your Reverence. Accommodation for two hundred people. Our main hall converted into a temple, to your specifications."

"It is good," said the Guru.

"It is good," echoed those of his followers within earshot.

"Somethin' odd about these bastards, Skipper," whispered Williams to Grimes.

"Mphm. Yes." The Commodore looked at the members of the Church of the Gateway as they trooped past him. They walked as though they were in a state of trance, gliding over the hard-packed red sand somnambulistically. Every face, young, not so young, or old, male or female, wore the same expression of . . . of beatitude? *When the saints go marching in,* thought Grimes irreverently, *I don't want to be of their number.*

Clavering came down the ramp from the forward airlock, letting the escalator do all the work. He looked very worried. He started to walk to where

Larwood was still talking with the Guru and his party, then paused where Grimes, Williams, and Billinghurst were standing.

Grimes said, "Nice Sunday School Outing you have here, Captain."

Clavering almost snarled, "That's not funny, Commodore!" then hurried on.

"What's bitin' *him?*" asked Williams.

"The same as what's just starting to nibble me, probably," Grimes told him. "Are you like me, Commander Williams? Do *you* feel uncomfortable when you're among really pious people, men and women who evince a passionate belief in something utterly irrational? Have you ever tried to argue with some fanatical true believer who's doing his damnedest to convert you to his own brand of hogwash? That's the way I feel now, looking at this bunch."

"Live an' let live," said Williams airily.

"I quite agree. That's the viewpoint of the cynical, tolerant agnostic. But don't forget that it's always been the overly religious who've taken a righteous delight in the slaughter of nonbelievers. Crusades, Jehads, bloody revolutions to establish the dictatorship of the proletariat—you name it, they've done it."

"I think these are a harmless bunch, Skipper, even if they are a bit odd. No more than rather elderly Blossom People with a few extra trimmings. Just spheres who're a bit too stiff in the joints for any really hearty rolling."

"Mphm. You could be right. I hope you are right." He turned to look at the devils who were bringing passengers' baggage ashore. "They don't seem to have much gear with them, do they?''

"Don't suppose they need much," said Williams. "Just a change of robes an' a spare pair o' sandals. A tube of depilatory cream for the sheilas. That's all. Somethin' to be said for travellin' light."

Billinghurst broke into the conversation. He said, "Well, Commodore, the balloon should be going up at any time now."

"What balloon?" asked Grimes, just to be awkward.

"*You* know," growled the fat man. "As long as you're ready to do what has to be done when it goes up."

"If it goes up," corrected Grimes.

"It will, Commodore, it will."

Grimes said to Williams as the Chief Collector moved ponderously away, "I hate to have to say it, but I'm afraid he's right."

It was, however, all of five days before the balloon did go up.

Those five days were . . . interesting. The People of the Gateway did not behave as the previous tourists had done. They went on no sightseeing tours. They did not frequent the Gambling Hell, neither did they simmer and freeze themselves in the hot and cold pools. They infuriated the Chef by demanding very plain foods, although their consumption of alcoholic drinks was far from low. Morning, afternoon and evening they met in the made-over dining hall, which they called their temple. They made no attempt to convert outsiders, but neither did they refuse admission to the curious.

Grimes attended one or two services, of course, as

did Williams and *Rim Malemute's* officers, and Billinghurst and his people, and the human staff of Inferno Valley. There was no singing, no sermonizing. The worshippers sat on the floor, in near-darkness, around the central dais on which the Guru William was seated. Every time he would open proceedings by "Brethren, let us meditate. Let us open our minds to the true reality." There would be silence, often a long silence, broken only by the subdued sound of breathing. Then somebody would utter a single word, such as, "Peace." Another silence. "Darkness everlasting." Silence again, and a growing tension. "The end of light." "The end of life." "Not-life, not-death." More silence. "The Gateway to Infinity." "Open the gate, open the gate, open the gate!" "The Gateway to Never." "Open the gate!"

"Gives me the willies, Skipper," Williams confessed to Grimes.

"I prefer religions that go in for Moody and Sankey style hymns," said the Commodore.

"Yeah. At least you can fit your own kind o' words to most o' the tunes." He began to sing untunefully,

> "Whiter than the whitewash on the wall!
> Whiter than the whitewash on the wall!
> Wash me in the water
> Where yer wash yer dirty daughter
> An' I shall be whiter than the whitewash
> On the wall!"

"Please, Commander.

"Sorry, Skipper. But sittin' crosslegged among that bunch o' morbid hopheads makes me wanter relax with a spot o' light blasphemy when I get outside. An' you said that you liked Moody an' Sankey.''

"I'm not so sure that I do, now. Meanwhile, what do our spies report?"

"Captain Clavering's aircar is ready to lift off at a second's notice. So are all the coaches. An' so is our work boat. Clavering's buggy is still bugged. Absolutely no joy with any of our radio equipment. But I have the boys on watches, an' they'll let us know at once if an' when anything happens."

"And our friend Billinghurst has his boys and girls on watches too. But I think that if Clavering does lift off to a rendezvous with SB Three it will be either around dawn or sunset."

"An' Mrs. Clavering? What's she sayin' these days?"

"Nothing much. Nothing much at all. She's worried stiff, of course. She did sort of hint that this would be the very last time, and that if I called my dogs off I should be . . . er . . . adequately recompensed." He grinned wrily. "Unluckily Billinghurst's dogs are in the hunt as well as mine, and I can't imagine any woman wanting to be nice to Billinghurst."

"People have probably said the same about you, Skipper."

"Remind me, Commander," said Grimes, "to have you busted down to Spaceman Fourth Class when we get back to civilization."

29

The balloon went up at dawn.

Substituting literal for metaphorical language, Clavering's private atmosphere flier lifted off at dawn. Grimes and his officers were already standing to, although none of them had incurred suspicion by venturing outside their hotel rooms with the exception of the watchkeeper aboard *Rim Malemute*. The young man hurried to the Lucifer Arms to inform the others that Clavering was on his way—to where?—but Grimes, even through the double, air-filled skin of his sleeping quarters, had heard the unmistakable irregular beat of an inertial drive unit.

The plan of operations was put into effect at once. The watch officer ran back to *Rim Malemute* and switched on the NST transceiver. This was still useless insofar as the reception or transmission of messages were concerned, but it was capable of jamming. He then carefully jockeyed the tug's work boat out of its bay, brought it to the landing ground in front of the Lucifer Arms.

Meanwhile Williams and his Chief Officer, both armed with stunguns, had gone to the hangar in which the resort's aircoaches were garaged. When Grimes and Billinghurst entered the building it was to hear Williams saying to Larwood, "I hereby requisition these vehicles for service in the Rim Worlds Navy."

"Stop playing at pirates, Commander Williams!" growled Larwood. "You've no legal right to do anything of the sort. These coaches are the property of a citizen of the Federation!"

Grimes intervened. "Mr. Larwood," he said. "I can, quite legally, requisition these vehicles—and I am doing so. I shall give you a receipt, and there will be adequate compensation."

"Legally? Come off it, Commodore."

"Yes. Legally. I am empowered to requisition any air or space vehicles of Rim Worlds registration for naval service. I can't touch your precious *Sally Ann* or her boats—she's Federation registry. But your coaches . . . *they* are licensed to carry passengers by the Confederacy."

"You bloody space lawyer!"

Sally Clavering had appeared on the scene. Her face was pale and drawn. She said, "Don't argue, Ron. It'll get us nowhere. *He* has the law on his side." The look she shot at Grimes should have shriveled him up where he stood.

He said, meaning it, "I'm sorry, Sally."

"You should be. For your information, just in case you're interested, Ian has gone to have it out with Drongo Kane, to tell him to find somebody else to handle his trade at this end, on one of the other Rim Worlds." She addressed herself to Billinghurst now, as well as to Grimes. "But Ian has broken no laws, and you know it."

"Did you say Drongo Kane?" demanded Grimes. *So his had been the oddly familiar voice recorded by Denise Dalgety.*

"Yes."

"And would the name of his ship be *Southerly Buster?*"

"Yes. *Southerly Buster III.*"

"Come on, Commodore." Billinghurst was impatient. "We can't afford to waste any time."

"I know, I know. And I know now whom we're up against. And I don't like it." He grinned. "Or perhaps I do. There're a few old scores to settle!"

Grimes took the work boat up. He hoped that by this time Clavering would be sufficiently distant for the small craft to be beyond the range of his radar. He hovered above Inferno Valley, making altitude slowly, until the commandeered air coach had lifted above the canyon rim. It was not possible for him to exchange any words with Williams, who was piloting the vehicle; the interference being broadcast by *Rim Malemute's* defective transceiver inhibited any sort of communication. In any case, it would have been advisable to maintain radio silence. Would this jamming effect the functioning of the transponder? Grimes had been assured that it would not, but he was not sure until he saw that the needle of the compass-like indicator had steadied on to a definite heading. He looked into his radar screen. There was nothing but ground clutter. Good. If he could not "see" Clavering, then Clavering could not "see" him.

He turned the boat on to the indicated heading, gave her maximum forward thrust. She vibrated frighteningly, excessively, but she went. He put her on to automatic pilot. It was awkward, he was beginning to find, to have to do everything himself. He had become far too used, over the years, to the control rooms of ships, with attentive officers at his eyes and hands. He felt that he could do with at least three pairs of the former and two of the latter. He looked into his radar screen again. The coach was following him. He transferred his attention to the gyro compass, then to the chart. Clavering, it seemed, was making for Dante's Pass. So Kane's landing place was somewhere in the Painted Badlands.

He looked out through the viewscreens—out, ahead and down. The dawn lull wasn't lasting. Below him the surface of the desert was obscured by driving clouds of red sand; ahead, the Great Smokies were all but invisible. It was obvious, too, that the boat was sagging very badly to leeward. He returned to his instruments to make the necessary course adjustment. He knew that Williams, an excellent pilot, would be doing the same—if he had not already done so.

Another course adjustment. . . .

He thought, *The little bitch is going sideways*.

And was that the Great Smokies showing up in the radar screen? It must be. Still there was no sign of Clavering, although the indicator needle jerked to starboard, showing that he had entered the Pass.

And if I keep him ahead, thought Grimes, stopping himself from changing course, *I shall pile up on Mount Beatrice*.

He made the necessary adjustments to his radar. Yes, there they were, Dante and Beatrice, marking the entrance to the Pass, steadily approaching the centre of the screen. He changed to a shorter range setting, and a shorter one, put the boat back on to manual steering. The wheel, mounted on the control column, bucked in his hands. The little craft had been designed to be used in airless space rather than in an atmosphere, a turbulent atmosphere at that. Williams, he thought with a twinge of jealousy, would be having a far better time of it in his air coach.

Hell! That's too bloody close!

Grimes yanked the control column violently to port, applying lateral thrust. Through his starboard window he saw black, steaming rocks dropping away from him. He must have missed them by the thickness of a coat of paint. He jerked the column to starboard as he saw, through a rift in the billowing smoke and steam, one of Mount Dante's minor craters almost below him. Hastily he reduced speed, hoping that Williams would not overtake him and crash into his stern.

He threaded his way through the pass on radar, breathed a great sigh of relief when he was out and clear. He would have liked to have got out his pipe, but he dared not take his hands from the controls. He flew through the last of the heavy smoke and steam into relatively clear air—but only relatively clear. Although on this side of the Smokies it was almost

359

calm, some freak of atmospheric circulation had brought down a thick haze, a yellow murk through which the fantastic rock formations looked menacingly. And Grimes was obliged to make a rock-hopping approach, as was Williams astern of him. If they flew above the eroded monoliths they would be picked up by Drongo Kane's radar. The master smuggler was not a man to neglect precautions.

Grimes watched his indicator needle, keeping Clavering ahead as much as possible. At the same time he watched his radar screen and tried to keep a visual lookout. Afterwards, when he told the story, he would say, "If the Venus of Milo had been equipped with arms I'd have knocked them off—and I as near as dammit castrated the Colossus of Eblis!" This was exaggeration, but only slightly so.

On he flew, and on, perspiring inside the protective suit that he was wearing, his hands clenched on the wheel, his attention divided between the indicator needle, the radar screen, the forward window of his cramped cabin and the chart of the area, one blown up from the brochure issued to tourists. He passed as close as he dared to the rock formations so that he could sight them visually and identify them. Now and again, caught by a freak eddy, he had to apply vertical or lateral thrust, or both together. The work boat complained but kept on going.

Then, ahead on the radar screen but still obscured by the haze, loomed a great mass. There was only one formation that it could be, and that was Ayers Rock. But surely the Rock did not have a much smaller monolith just over a kilometre to the east of it.

Grimes decided not to reduce speed. By so doing he could well forfeit the advantage of surprise. He ignored his radar, concentrated on a visual lookout. And, at last, there, on his port bow, was the sullenly brooding mass of red granite and, right ahead, indistinct but clearer with every passing second, the silvery spire of a grounded spaceship. By the foot of the ramp from her after airlock was a small atmosphere craft.

The Commodore applied maximum forward thrust and, at the same time, using one hand, worked his respirator over his head. He put the boat on full reverse when he was almost up to and over Clavering's craft. He cut the drive, slammed down heavily on to the red sand. He was out of the door and running for the ramp before the dust had settled. He was dimly aware that Williams, just behind him, had brought the coach in to a hasty landing.

It was too much to hope for—but it seemed that his arrival had been neither seen nor heard. The airlock outer door remained open, the ramp remained extended. He pulled his stungun from its holster as he ran up the gangway. Impatiently he waited for Williams and Billinghurst to join him in the chamber of the airlock; it was too small to hold more than three men. The others—*Rim Malemute's* people and the Customs officers—would have to wait their turn.

Williams used the standard controls to shut the outer door, to evacuate the foul air of Eblis and to introduce the clean air of the ship into the chamber. All this must be registering on the remote control board in the control room, but perhaps there was no officer on duty there. He pushed the knob that would open the inner door.

It opened.

A tall figure stood on the other side of it to receive them—a big man who, if he lost only a little weight, could be classified as skinny. His face, under the stubble of greyish yellow hair, was deeply tanned and seamed, and looked as though at some time in the past it had been completely shattered and then reassembled not too carefully.

He said, "Welcome aboard, Commander Grimes! I beg your pardon, *Commodore* Grimes. But I always think of you as that boy scoutish Survey Service Lieutenant Commander who was captain of *Seeker*."

Grimes removed his respirator with the hand that was not holding the gun. "Captain Kane," he said, "you are under arrest, and your ship is seized."

"Am I, now? Is she, now? Let's not be hasty, Commander—Commodore, I mean. What will the Federation say when it hears that a breakaway colonial officer has arrested one of its shipmasters? Suppose we have a yarn about old times first, Commodore. Come on up to my dogbox to see how the poor live. This is Liberty Hall—you can spit on the mat an' call the cat a bastard!"

"I'd rather not accept your hospitality, Captain Kane, in these circumstances. Or in any circumstances."

"Still the same stuffy bastard, ain't yer, Grimes? But if yer seizin' *Southerly Buster III*—I still haven't forgiven yer fer what yer did ter the first

Southerly Buster—yer'll have ter see her papers. Register, Articles o' Agreement an' all the rest of it."

"He's right," said Billinghurst.

"Ain't yer goin' ter introduce me to yer cobbers, Commodore?"

"This is Mr. Billinghurst," said Grimes curtly, "Chief Collector of Customs for the Confederacy. And this is Commander Williams, of the Rim Worlds Navy."

"The way I'm surrounded," drawled Kane. "I suppose I should surrender. But I ain't goin' to. I . . ."

Whatever else he said was drowned by the sudden clamour of *Southerly Buster's* inertial drive as she lifted with vicious acceleration, as she staggered under the sudden application of lateral thrust that threw the three unprepared men heavily to the deck.

Kane's stungun was out, and a couple of tough looking characters, similarly armed, had put in an appearance.

Speaking loudly to be heard above the irregular beat of the drive Kane said cheerfully, "An' if he's doin' what he was told ter do, my gunnery boy's just in the act o' vaporizin' your transport with his pet laser cannon. I hope none o' your nongs are still inside that coach they came in."

But he didn't seem to be worrying much about it.

30

"An' now," drawled Drongo Kane, "what am I goin' ter do with you bastards?"

"Return us to Inferno Valley!" snapped Grimes.

Kane lazily surveyed his prisoners—Clavering, Grimes, Billinghurst and Williams, the officers from *Rim Malemute*, the Customs sub-inspectors. He said, leering in Denise Dalgety's direction, "Seems a cryin' shame ter throw a good blonde back ter where she came from, don't it?"

The girl flushed angrily and Williams snarled, "That's enough o' that, Kane!"

"Is it, now, Commander? Get it inter yer thick head—an' that goes for all o' yer—that there ain't a thing any o' yer can do."

And there's not, thought Grimes. *Not until this paralysis wears off. And it won't, as long as these goons keep giving us extra shots with their stunguns as soon as it looks like doing so.*

"In fact," Kane went on, "I think I deserve some reward for goin' back, for not leavin' Blondie an' the others wanderin' around in the desert." He extricated a gnarled cigar from the breast pocket of his uniform coverall, ostentatiously lit it with his laser pistol. It stank as bad as it looked.

"Release us at once!" blustered Billinghurst.

"An' wouldn't yer be peeved if I did, Chief Collector? What if I took yer at yer word, an' dumped yer down in the Painted Badlands, miles from anywhere, an' with no transport but yer own bleedin' hooves?" He exhaled a cloud of smoke. "But yer dead lucky. Clavering here won't play ball, so I have ter go all the way ter Inferno Valley in person, singin' an' dancin', ter make me own deal with the boss cocky o' that bunch o' holy joes. Church o' the Gateway, ain't it? They want dreamy weed, I've got it. They can have it, at my price." He fixed his attention on Grimes. "Ever hear o' Australis, Commodore? Not Austral. Australis. A frontier planet like these worlds o' yours, only 'stead o' bein' on the Rim it's way out to hell an' gone beyond the south rotor bearin' o' the Galaxy. Did a sim'lar deal there, wi' some bunch o' religious nuts. They had a guru, too. Often wonder what happened. Been no news out o' Australis fer quite some time. Could be that the world itself ain't there any more. After I heard the guru's advance spiel about what he said was goin' ter be the final act o' worship, acceptance an' all the rest of it I decided ter get the hell out." He grinned. "Tell yer what. I'll return yer all ter Inferno Valley, an' insist that this Guru William try ter make converts o' yer. If he won't play he gets no dreamy weed."

"The users of it," remarked Billinghurst, "claim that dreamy weed is non-addictive."

Keep out of it, you stupid, fat slob! thought Grimes.

"So 't'is, Chief Collector. So 't'is. Smoked it once myself—try anythin' once, that's me. Guess I've the wrong kind o' mind. Didn't see visions or dream dreams. But I'm a baddie, an' you're all goodies."

Clavering said, "There will be no business transactions of any kind on *my* world."

"An' who's goin' ter stop me from doin' business? Not you, fer a start. You were pleased enough ter take yer rake-off from my deals until that silly bitch got blown up, weren't yer? Oh, well, go an' stew in yer own juice with the other goodies."

Grimes realized that sensation was coming back into his hands and feet, that he could move his fingers and toes. He mentally measured the distance between himself and the arrogant Drongo Kane, and between Kane and the three armed spacemen lounging negligently in the doorways of the ship's saloon. There was a chance, he thought. There was a chance, and if he could use Kane's body as a shield it might be a good one.

"Mr. Welland," drawled Drongo Kane, "yer might give the . . . er . . . passengers a sprayin' over with yer stungun. I noticed the Commodore twitchin' his pinkie just now."

The weapon, set on low power, buzzed softly. Grimes' nerves tingled, then went dead. He could breathe, he could move his eyes, he could speak, even, but that was all.

"I'll give yer all a stronger dose before we land,"

Kane promised them. "The Guru an' his boys an' girls can carry yer off me ship."

"You'll be sorry for this," promised Grimes.

"I shan't be when I count the foldin' money that Guru William's goin' ter hand over ter me," Kane assured him. "Or, if I am, I shall cry all the way ter the bank."

Kane left then, presumably to take over the pilotage of his ship. The three guards remained. They sneered at Billinghurst's offer of a free pardon, a reward even, if they assisted the forces of law and order. They laughed loudly when Denise Dalgety made an appeal to their decency as human beings. Welland, who seemed to be Kane's Second Mate, exclaimed, "We ain't decent, lady; if we were we wouldn't be in Drongo's rustbucket. If yer want ter find out just how indecent we can be. . . ."

"No!" she cried. "You wouldn't!"

"Wouldn't I, honey?"

But he didn't, though it was obvious that it was fear of Kane that restrained him rather than any respect for the girl.

Grimes, listening to the varying beat of the inertial drive, was trying to work out where they were. They were flying through severe turbulence, that much was obvious. He said to Clavering, "Has Kane been to Inferno Valley before?"

"Only as a passenger, Commodore. And only in my flier, usually during the evening lull."

"Mphm. Will he be able, do you think, to get down into the valley with the winds on top at gale force, at least?"

"You did, Commodore."

"In a much smaller ship."

Welland guffawed scornfully. "The Old Man could take this bitch through hell without singeing her hide! But stow the gab, will yer? Yer none o' yer sparklin' conversationalists!"

"For the last time . . ." began Billinghurst, making a final attempt to enlist aid from this unlikely quarter.

"Aw, shaddup!"

The stunguns buzzed, and breathing became almost impossible, and talking quite impossible.

Grimes could still think, and he could hear. There were surges of power as lateral thrust was applied one way and the other, then diminution of the irregular beat as vertical thrust was reduced.

Southerly Buster III was coming in for a landing.

31

Those who had been Kane's prisoners were seated in a group to one side of the huge dining hall, and with them were Sally Clavering and the members of Clavering's staff. These, too, had been incapacitated by judicious use of the stunguns. Drongo Kane had collected his payment from the Guru William and had gone, the noisy hammering of his inertial drive echoing back and forth between the sheer cliffs of the valley's walls until it had suddenly faded into silence.

Kane was gone—but the Guru William remained.

He was a harmless man—to judge by his appearance—saintly, even. He had stood over the nonbelievers after they had been dragged and carried into his temple and had looked at them for long minutes, a faint smile curving his mouth, his huge, brown eyes looking through and beyond the helpless men and women. He murmured, "Peace."

Grimes tried to say something, anything, but could not. He would be voiceless until the paralysis wore off.

"Peace," murmured the guru again, but in a

louder tone. "Peace. The last, the everlasting peace. And you, my sons and my daughters, are blessed, for you shall see, with us, the cessation of all that is harsh, all that is discordant."

Billinghurst managed to make some sort of noise. "Blahh . . . blahh."

"I must leave you, my sons and my daughters, my brethren, my sisters. The worship, the last act of worship, of acceptance, is to begin. Surrender yourselves. Join with us, the People of the Gateway. The gateway is about to be opened."

On to what? Grimes demanded of himself desperately. *On to what?* More than any of the others, with the possible exception of Williams, he was starting to realize the implications of it all. He tried to hold his breath as he smelled the sweet yet acrid taint that was beginning to pervade the air in the dome, reasoning that the smoke of burning dreamy weed was being blown in through the airconditioning system. He wondered how much the Guru William had paid for the consignment. A small fortune—or a large one—must be smoldering away somewhere behind the scenes.

Williams had mounted the dais and, surrounded by acolytes, was squatting there in the lotus posture. The bald heads of the women glimmered eerily in the dim light. Their eyes, and the eyes of the men, seemed to be self-luminous. Drifting streamers of grey fog curled about them.

"We accept . . ." intoned the Guru.

"We accept . . ." repeated his flock. The words had a faraway sound, like a thin, cold wind rustling the detritus of long dead years.

"The nothingness . . ."

"The nothingness . . ."

"Beyond the stars."

"Beyond the stars."

The nothingness, or the otherness, thought Grimes. Here, out on the Rim, on the very edge of the expanding galaxy, the skin of the bubble that held the continuum was stretched almost to bursting, the barriers between the dimensions were flimsy, almost nonexistent. There were, Grimes knew all too well, the other time tracks, the alternate universes. And what—if anything—lay between the time tracks, the universes?

"Open the Gateway . . ."

"The Gateway to Never . . ."

I will not believe, Grimes told himself. *I will* not *believe.*

The effects of the last stungun shock were wearing off now, but the fumes of the consciousness-expanding drug were taking effect. On the dais the guru's form was outlined by an aura, not of light, nor yet of darkness, but of *nothingness.*

And the word beat in the Commodore's mind, *Never . . . never . . . never. . . .* Those about him were becoming insubstantial, filmy. . . . He lifted his hand—and realized with horror that he could see through it, that he was looking through skin and flesh and bone at the calm, the impossibly calm face of Pahvani.

"Nirvana . . ." the young sub-inspector was murmuring. "Nirvana. . . ."

And was this what had happened on Australis, *to* Australis? Was this why Drongo Kane had gotten

371

away and clear like a bat out of hell? The picture that
formed in Grimes' mind of a huge, black, winged
mammal beating its way through and between
towering columns of crimson fire was as real as
though he were actually seeing it—and it was better
than that *nothingness* which was showing through
the widening rents in the very continuum.

"Open the Gateway. . . ."

"The Gateway to Never . . ."

"Accept, accept. . . ."

I'm damned *if I'll accept,* thought Grimes.

Light was beating upwards in waves—red,
orange, dazzling blue-white—from the core of the
planet, washing over and through Grimes' body like
cool water, dissipating itself in the utterly starless
dark, the dark that was a negation of everything, all
around, light that fought a losing battle against the
nothingness, that faded, faster and faster, to a faint,
ashy glimmer. He put out his hand, or thought that he
put out his hand, to catch one of the last, feeble
photons, held it in his cupped palm, stared at the
dying, weakly pulsating thing and willed it to survive. It flared fitfully, and . . .

Somebody had hold of his sleeve, was shaking it.
Somebody was saying, almost hissing, "Sir, sir!"

Grimes stared at the intrusive being. So this was
what lay in the nothingness between the time tracks.
It was hell, the old-fashioned hell of the fundamen-
talist faiths at which he had always sneered, a hell
peopled by horrendous, horned and tailed demons.
. . .

"Sir! Sir! Come back, please!"

Come *back?* What the hell was this stupid devil yapping about? How could he come back when he was only just getting there?

"Sir! Earthquake. Bad one!"

"Go away . . . go away. . . ."

The scaled, clawed hands were at his face, were forcing something over his head. Grimes drew in a panicky breath, and the sudden inhalation of almost pure oxygen nearly choked him. He put up his hands to try to tear off the respirator, but there were devils all around him, restraining him. He was aware that the floor was heaving underfoot, and he was fighting as much to retain his balance as to throw off his assailants.

His assailants?

His saviors.

The floor was like a calm sea over which a long, low swell was rolling, and the walls of the dome were bellying inwards. But only Grimes and his attendant demons were aware of this—and he still wondered if this were actuality or some drug-induced vision. Billinghurst squatted there like a Buddha, and beside him young Pahvani was staring into—or *at*—nothingness, a supernaturally sweet smile on his thin face. Williams was muttering, "The Outback. The last Outback. . . ." And Sally Clavering . . . was that a halo faint-gleaming about her head, or was it merely a wreathing streamer of dreamy weed smoke?

And were Billinghurst and Williams and the others as insubstantial as the guru and his people? They were all fading, fading fast, as they swayed in time to the waves that swept across the floor in regular undulations. They were fading—and again, through rents in the very fabric of space-time, that ultimate, horrifying *nothingness* was increasingly evident.

If only the simple, three dimensional fabric of the dome would rend, to release the hallucinogenic fumes. . . .

What was hallucination, and what was not?

"Sir, sir!" It was the devil who had first pulled Grimes back to reality, or to what passed for reality. "Sir, sir! *Do* something, please! We are frightened."

You aren't the only one, thought Grimes.

He looked at the native. He must have been a kitchen helper of some kind. He was wearing an incongruous white apron, and a belt with a pouch into which were thrust various tools.

"Give me your knife," ordered the Commodore.

He grabbed the implement, used it to tear away the black hangings shrouding the interior wall of the dome. Behind these the plastic was tough, too tough, even though the knife was razor-sharp. And then . . . and then the wall bellied inwards as there was a particularly severe tremor and the skin was stretched almost to bursting.

The knife penetrated, and tore the outer skin as well. There was a great *whoosh* as the air rushed out, and Grimes and his helpers were blown through the opening into the night, into the night that was blessedly normal despite the earthquake shocks that continued, with increasing severity. He stood there, keeping his balance somehow, and watched in fascination as the fantastic bubble structure that was the Lucifer Arms collapsed upon itself, as balloon after glowing balloon deflated, some with explosive suddenness, some slowly. The generators kept working until the very end, and the darkness—the real darkness, the natural darkness—did not sweep in until the last bubble had burst.

Grimes had battery powered emergency lights brought from *Rim Malemute,* and then the rescue work began.

32

"I've just heard from Clavering," said Grimes to Sonya. "He and Sally didn't come out of it too badly. The Lucifer Arms was insured against earthquake damage, and Lloyd's paid up."

"Earthquake damage!" she scoffed. "Earthquake damage! When *you* were running amok with a long knife!"

"It wasn't all that long. And there was an earthquake, after all."

"Joking apart, John, what do you make of it all?"

"You've read my report."

"Yes. But I sort of gained the impression that you were too scared, still, to write what you really thought."

"Could be. Could be. You know, I keep thinking of the Lucifer Arms as a microcosm of the universe in which we live, our space-time continuum. What would have happened if the Guru William had succeeded in bursting the bubble of what we think of as reality, just as I burst that bubble of inflated plastic?"

"I can't see us all going whooshing out into nothingness."

"Can't you? The guru's body was never found, you know, or the bodies of about a hundred of his disciples. Or that of young Pahvani. They *could* have fallen into one of the fissures that opened and closed again—but it's odd that, apart from the utterly missing people, there were no casualties." He slowly filled and lit his pipe. "An unfortunate business. Clavering and his people will have to leave the Rim, of course. Billinghurst's a vindictive bastard. Drongo Kane'll get away scot free. He broke no Federation laws, and I doubt very much if we could get him extradited to any of our worlds."

"And the Confederacy," she said, "will be confirmed in its archaic puritanism insofar as the permissive practices of the Federated planets are concerned."

"I hope that you're right," he said. "I sincerely hope that you're right." She looked at him in some amazement. He laughed. "No, I'm not becoming a wowser in my old age. It's just that I've been made to realize that even if what you do doesn't much matter, *where* you do it does.

"To use the so-called mind-expanding drugs out here, on the Rim, is like smoking over a powder barrel!"

"The sort of thing you'd do," she jeered, but without malice.

"But only tobacco," he told her, puffing away contentedly on his pipe. "But only tobacco."

There are a lot more
where this one came from!

THE GASHLYCRUMB TINIES

or, After the Outing

BY

Edward Gorey

Houghton Mifflin Harcourt

Boston   New York

For information about permission to reproduce selections from this book,
write to trade.permissions@hmhco.com or to Permissions, Houghton Mifflin Harcourt
Publishing Company, 3 Park Avenue, 19th Floor, New York, New York 10016.

www.hmhco.com

Library of Congress Cataloging-in-Publication Data
Gorey, Edward, 1925–
The Gashlycrumb tinies/by Edward Gorey.
p. cm.
ISBN 978-0-15-100308-2
1. English language—Alphabet—Humor.
2. American wit and humor, Pictorial. I. Title.
[PS3557.0753G37 1997]
741.5'973—dc21 97-22196
SC 35 34 33
4500614684
Printed in China

For Helne

A is for AMY who fell down the stairs

B is for BASIL assaulted by bears

C is for CLARA who wasted away

D is for DESMOND thrown out of a sleigh

E is for ERNEST who choked on a peach

F is for FANNY sucked dry by a leech

G is for GEORGE smothered under a rug

H is for HECTOR done in by a thug

I is for IDA who drowned in a lake

J is for JAMES who took lye by mistake

K is for KATE who was struck with an axe

L is for LEO who swallowed some tacks

M is for MAUD who was *swept out to sea*

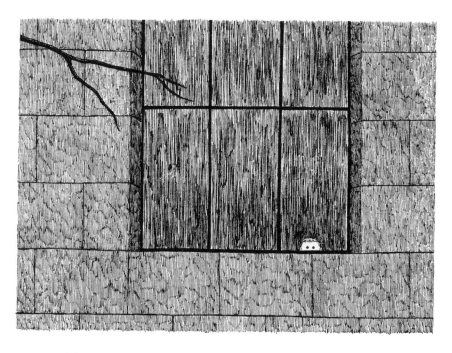

N is for NEVILLE who died of ennui

O is for OLIVE run through with an awl

P is for PRUE trampled flat in a brawl

Q is for QUENTIN who sank in a mire

R is for RHODA consumed by a fire

S is for SUSAN who perished of fits

T is for TITUS who flew into bits

U is for UNA who slipped down a drain

V is for VICTOR squashed under a train

W is for WINNIE embedded in ice

X is for XERXES devoured by mice

Y is for YORICK whose head was knocked in

Z is for ZILLAH who drank too much gin